# BIOLOGY

# BIOLOGY

## A Seventh-day Adventist Approach for Students and Teachers

H. Thomas Goodwin, Editor

Berrien Springs, Michigan

Andrews University Press
Sutherland House
8360 W. Campus Circle Dr.
Berrien Springs, MI 49104–1700 U.S.A.
Telephone: 269–471–6134
Fax: 269–471–6224
Email: aupo@andrews.edu
Website: http://universitypress.andrews.edu



ISBN 978–1–883925–93–2 (paperback)
ISBN 978–1–883925–96–3 (e-book)

Library of Congress Control Number: 2013956892

Printed in the United States of America
20 19 18 17 16 4 5 6 7 8

Publication of this book has been sponsored by:

The Institute for Christian Teaching
General Conference Education Department
12501 Old Columbia Pike
Silver Spring, MD 20904–6600, U.S.A.
Telephone: (301) 680–5060
Fax: (301) 622–9627
Website: http://ict.adventist.org
Email: rodrigueze@gc.adventist.org

The Center for College Faith
Andrews University
Berrien Springs, MI 49104 U.S.A.
Telephone: (269) 471–6291
Email: kutzner@andrews.edu

Typeset: 10.8/13.2 Times New Roman

# TABLE OF CONTENTS

# ABOUT THIS BOOK AND SERIES

This volume is one of an ongoing series about integrating faith with learning. The series is being co-sponsored by the Institute for Christian Teaching (ICT) at the Education Department of the General Conference of Seventh-day Adventists and the Center for College Faith (CCF) at Andrews University. While the present work concerns the teaching of biology, three previously published volumes have dealt with the teaching of history, literature, and sociology in an Adventist setting. Future books are anticipated.

All teaching in Seventh-day Adventist institutions has an overriding goal of building faith not only in the Christian message but also in the Adventist understanding of Christianity and in its mission to the world. However, Adventist schools teach a broad range of subject matter, much of which is generally thought of as secular. The Adventist teacher of biology must use a textbook that is written by scholars who are not necessarily believers and who might even be hostile to religion. The instructor must deal with material that on the surface does not appear to have spiritual value. How then can Adventist teachers of biology (or any other discipline) build faith in the essentials of Christianity and Adventism while at the same time covering the material essential for an understanding of the discipline?

This volume addresses that challenge. It is not intended to be a textbook in biology. The authors do not attempt to plumb its various sub-divisions. Rather it is a supplement to which teachers and students can turn for insights about how to weave faith into their study of biology. It holds that all truth is God's truth if only with the eye of faith we can see beneath the surface of the apparently secular and discern that God is working there also.

While the book is primarily intended for use by teachers and students pursuing biology in Adventist institutions of higher learning, it will also prove useful for Adventist students studying biology at non-Adventist colleges and universities. It is vital that these students emerge from their programs of study with heightened faith and a driving sense of mission for God and His world. It is with this hope and prayer that we publish this fourth volume in the series.

THE CENTER FOR COLLEGE FAITH BOARD

# FOREWORD

The present volume is the fourth in an ongoing series cosponsored by the General Conference Education Department and the Center for College Faith at Andrews University. This book helps readers consider how scientific evidence relates to the Bible and Seventh-day Adventist beliefs such as creation, human nature, the Sabbath, and the ongoing duty for stewardship of the earth, even while anticipating the return of Christ and a world made new.

The book goes beyond the creation-evolution debate and does not shrink from apparent conflicts between faith and reason. Such a discussion is possible because the authors reject the popular notion of non-overlapping magisteria, in which the domains of faith and of science simply don't intersect. Instead they deal with issues in biology from a biblical worldview. The result is an informed discussion and debate not found in standard textbooks.

While no theory is available that explains everything we see in nature, recent advances in science have increasingly revealed that our world shows striking evidence of design by an intelligent Creator. These observations are reasonably inferred as evidence for the kind of special creation described in Genesis and given prominence in the three angels' messages of Revelation 14.

Special thanks go to Roger Dudley, director of publications for the Center for College Faith at Andrews University, for shepherding the volume to completion, and to H. Thomas Goodwin, chair of the Department of Biology at Andrews University, for bringing the authors together, writing two chapters himself, and editing the book. The result is an illuminating discussion of science that affirms faith in a redemptive Creator.

Lisa M. Beardsley-Hardy, Director of Education
Seventh-day Adventist Church World Headquarters

# EDITOR'S PREFACE

Seventh-day Adventists have explored the relationship between science and our faith for over one hundred years, and many books have been published on the subject. What place is there, then, for yet another book in the discussion? That's a good question, and I'll offer two modest suggestions for how the present volume might contribute.

First, this book was written with a specific purpose and target audience: it is intended as a supplementary text or resource for Adventist college students of biology (although others may benefit as well). The book is a collection of essays—all written by Adventist biologists—designed to explore how Adventist faith and biology interface across a selection of content areas, and students will benefit most by reading these essays along with what they are learning in their college studies.

Second, this book intentionally seeks to broaden the dialogue between biology and Adventist faith to include, but extend beyond, the creation-evolution controversy—the topic that understandably dominates most Adventist contributions in the field. As we'll see, Adventist faith fruitfully interfaces with a variety of biological and related disciplines such as cognitive science, ecology, and conservation biology. Indeed, I will argue in chapter 1 that science (including biology) and Christian faith can be thought of as honest friends, partners who often support—but sometimes challenge—each other in the search for truth.

This volume is the fourth in a series that examines the interface between Adventist faith and academic disciplines (previous books have engaged history, literature, and sociology), but it differs from previous volumes in that it is a collection of essays rather than work by a single author. The choice was intentional; biology is a diverse, growing field, and we felt our readers would be served best if Adventist biologists who practice—and teach—in specific areas wrote chapters relevant to their fields of expertise.

The book series is cosponsored by the Center for College Faith at Andrews University and the Department of Education of the General Conference of Seventh-day Adventists, and I gratefully acknowledge the helpful role both entities have played in seeing the present volume to fruition.

Mickey Kutzner and Roger Dudley—director and general book editor, respectively, of the Center for College Faith—provided enthusiastic encouragement, and occasional prodding, as I assembled and edited the essays in this volume.

Garland Dulan and Lisa Beardsley-Hardy, past and current director of the General Conference Department of Education, likewise have supported the production of this volume, both conceptually and financially.

Andrews University Press has published all volumes in the series, and I especially thank Ronald Knott, director of the press, for publishing works such as this that contribute to Adventist higher education.

Most of the essays in this book were presented orally during the opening session of the 2009 Geoscience Research Institute Council (GRICO). Thanks to Jim Gibson, director at the Geoscience Research Institute, for making this venue available to us. Also, thanks to the participants at GRICO who listened and provided critical feedback.

Each essay in this volume was critically reviewed by six to nine Adventist scholars in relevant disciplines, and I am deeply indebted to them for their constructive feedback. Listed alphabetically, these reviewers are: D. Abbey, A. Archer, G. Atkins, L. Brand, R. Cushman, N. Donkor, J. Galusha, J. Gibson, J. Hayward, H. Rasi, A. Roth, R. Schafer, E. Schwab, D. Steen, D. Woodland, A. Wyrick, R. Zdor, and six anonymous reviewers. Thanks to all!

Most of all, I want to thank the authors who devoted substantial time and effort as they contributed to this book. While some authors forwarded arguments that I did not agree with (yes, Adventist biologists disagree on some things!), I believe all of the essays offer helpful insights to readers who seek to bring together their Adventist faith and knowledge of biology.

# Chapter One

# INTRODUCTION: SCIENCE AND FAITH AS HONEST FRIENDS

## H. Thomas Goodwin

I fell in love with biology as a junior in college when, as a theology major, I took two life-changing science courses. One course showed me how scientific knowledge and Adventist beliefs may interact and sometimes challenge each other. The other revealed the intricacies of living systems, from cells to ecosystems. I was hooked—and, after 20 years of college teaching and scientific research, I still am!

I enjoy all areas of biology, but my specialty is paleobiology, the study of ancient life as preserved in the fossil record. Paleobiology offers many rewards to the inquisitive, and I've enjoyed my share—for example, the thrill of discovering extinct species previously unknown to science. (Most of my work has focused on fossil squirrels, *not* dinosaurs. Really.) Paleobiology also raises puzzling questions for Seventh-day Adventist scholars that we will explore in chapter 5. How do we account for the strange, extinct creatures of long ago in light of the biblical creation narratives? What do the fossils tell us about God's work of creation?

Questions such as these encourage us to explore the ways that Adventist beliefs and biological knowledge inform, interact, and sometimes challenge each other, and that is the task of this book. As we will see, a Seventh-day Adventist perspective has bearing on a wide range of biological topics. Separate essays will probe the interactions between Adventist beliefs and genomics, the biology of human consciousness, evolution, the fossil record, ecology, and environmental stewardship, although these topics represent only a sample of possible points of engagement. We'll see throughout the book that, although important challenges exist, Adventist beliefs and scientific discoveries often illuminate each other in helpful ways.

Before we move to these specific topics, however, we need to step back to see the big picture when it comes to the interactions between Adventist beliefs and science (including biology). That is the task of this essay, and I hope to convince you of three points. First, I will argue that core Christian beliefs shared by Seventh-day Adventists give critical insight into the power and limits of science as a way of knowing. Second, I will claim that scientific knowledge often enriches theological beliefs, particularly beliefs about God as creator and humans as creatures formed in God's image. Third, I will argue that, although scientific knowledge sometimes challenges Adventist beliefs, these challenges should not surprise us and provide opportunity for scientific, theological, and ethical growth. In sum, I will make the case that science and Adventist faith may function as honest friends—supportive but sometimes challenging each other.

Although the analogy of honest friendship yields helpful insights, it does have limits: Adventists do not approach the science-faith dialogue with neutrality. We acknowledge the Bible as "the authoritative revealer of doctrines, and the trustworthy record of God's acts in history" (fundamental belief 1, in part; General Conference of Seventh-day Adventists 2005), and this commitment shapes our understanding of nature. It also undergirds our approach in this book, as we explore the dynamic relationship between science and Adventist faith.

## Defining a Christian Perspective on the Nature of Science

Before we explore the relationship between biblical beliefs and science, we need to clarify what science is and how it works. Roughly, science is a way to gain knowledge about nature that seeks to describe and explain phenomena of the material world—the world of atoms and molecules, organisms and ecosystems, planets and stars—in ways that other scientists can test empirically. Ecologists, for example, record which species are present in an ecosystem, when and where the species are active, how the various species interact with each other and with the physical environment—and then try to explain all these observations in terms of theories about limiting factors, competition, energy flow, and so on. Each of these descriptions and explanations can be tested by other scientists who wish to repeat the relevant experiments or observations, an important element of quality control in science.

By its very nature, scientific knowledge is dynamic and always changing, driven by the ongoing interaction of three core elements of scientific thought (Fig. 1): data, theories, and shaping principles (Ratzsch 1996:120–128). Data

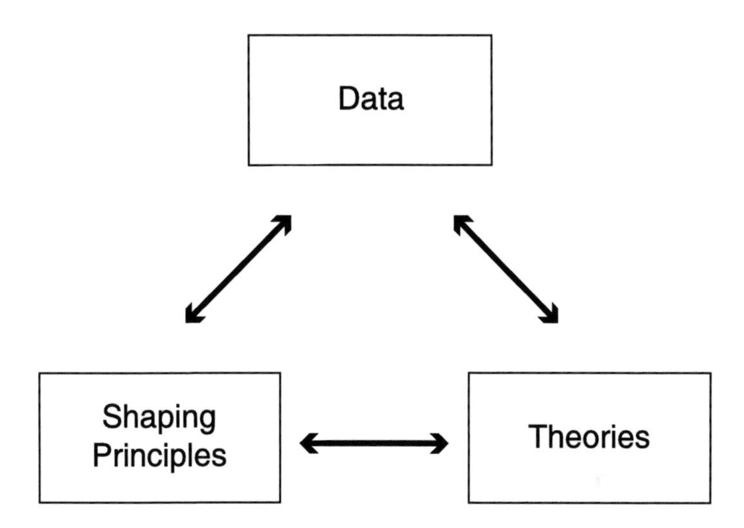


**Figure 1**—Concept map depicting 3 interacting components of scientific thought (after Ratzsch 1996). Note that *theory* as used here refers to any explanatory idea in science: from a tentative hypothesis to a well-established theory.

represent the observations, counts, and measurements that scientists record and wish to explain. Theories[1] are the ideas scientists develop to make sense of and interpret their data. Shaping principles correspond to background beliefs, commitments, and values that inevitably influence a scientist's work, often unconsciously. Members of a given scientific community typically share a broad set of core theories and shaping principles that strongly guides their work—the types of data they look for, the kinds of explanations they propose, and so on. Thomas Kuhn (1970), a noted philosopher of science, referred to these broadly shared sets of theories and shaping principles as *paradigms*.

Much of this dynamism in scientific thought is driven by the interaction of data and theory as scientists—usually working within a particular paradigm—seek to find a better fit between what they observe in nature and their theories about nature. Sometimes change occurs because a fruitful theory (often combined with new methods) encourages accumulation of new data. A prime example is the exponential increase in genome sequence data over the past decade, fuelled by modern theories

1. I use *theory* here in the sense it is employed by Del Ratzsch: as any explanatory idea in science, from a tentative hypothesis to a well-established theory.

of genetics and new methods of DNA sequencing. At other times, change occurs because new data force us to revise or even replace an existing theory. Tim Standish offers a personal example in chapter 2: his interpretation about the number of genes in the human genome changed overnight—literally—with publication of new data (the draft sequence of the human genome). In both cases, the dynamic development of scientific knowledge requires that theory and data remain in dialogue with each other.

According to Thomas Kuhn, scientific knowledge sometimes changes in a more holistic and comprehensive manner. In this view, scientists normally do not question their paradigms; they assume them to be true and do science accordingly. In the process, however, scientists will occasionally discover things that don't fit the expectations of the paradigm. If these discoveries are sufficiently serious or numerous, a scientific discipline will experience a *crisis* as scientists scramble to make sense of the anomalous data. During a crisis, a brilliant scientist may come up with a whole new way of looking at the discipline—a new paradigm. If the new paradigm works well, over time the community will "switch over" from the old to the new; a *scientific revolution* will occur (Kuhn 1970). Kuhn suggested that such episodes represent important events in the history of science because they open up new vistas of research, generate new and more comprehensive theories, and stimulate scientists to study a new range of phenomena. Kuhn's ideas may be oversimplified—especially in fast-paced disciplines characterized by perpetual "crisis" and multiple, competing hypotheses—but they offer helpful insights into the way scientific thinking has progressed over time.

All scientific disciplines share a commitment to empirical testability, but disciplines vary in how they collect data and test theories. At risk of oversimplification, the *experimental* sciences (e.g., physics, chemistry, and many areas of biology) typically test hypotheses by doing multiple, controlled experiments under differing conditions. In contrast, the *historical* sciences (e.g., paleontology and archaeology) usually cannot directly test causal hypotheses by experiment. Rather, they seek to decipher *past* causes (for example, causes of the extinction of mammoths at the end of the Ice Age—see chapter 5) by proposing multiple, competing hypotheses and looking for physical evidence that will discriminate among these hypotheses (Cleland 2001)—a form of hypothesis testing. This difference in method may have important implications, as we'll see later in this chapter. (See chapter 8 by Earl Aagaard for an extended discussion of the distinction between experimental and historical sciences.)

To recap, I understand science to be a way to gain testable knowledge about nature, a method that drives the continuous accumulation of knowledge within paradigms as well as the occasional scientific revolution in which one paradigm replaces another. How do Christian beliefs help us understand this way of knowing? We will now explore what Christian beliefs may tell us about the power and limits of science.

### *The Power of Science*

Science is a powerful way to gain knowledge about nature, a power demonstrated by two facts. First, scientific theories often unify diverse observations in elegant and simple ways and commonly make surprising predictions about nature that turn out to be valid, especially in the experimental sciences. Einstein's general theory of relativity, for example, unified broad areas of physics with mathematical elegance (or so I'm told, being neither a mathematician nor a physicist!). It also made surprising and risky predictions—for example, that light should bend when it passes a large object with strong gravitational force—predictions that later were verified experimentally. When scientific theories unify and accurately predict what we see (and should see) in this way, we gain some confidence that science teaches us something real about the world.

Second, the power of science is demonstrated by the practical utility of scientific theories. Science generated the theoretical knowledge that made it possible for humans to land on (and return safely from) the moon, develop treatments for malaria, eradicate smallpox, exponentially increase crop production per acre, and create iPhones and personal computers. Again, when our theories are so useful, we gain some confidence (although never certainty) that science is telling us something real about nature.

This demonstrated power of science—to unify and predict many things we see in nature through theories that often have profound practical usefulness—raises an intriguing question. Why does science work so well? Eugene Wigner, a theoretical physicist, engaged this question when he marveled at the "unreasonable effectiveness of mathematics" as a way to unify what we know about physics. He went on to describe this ability as "a wonderful gift which we neither understand nor deserve" (Wigner

1960:14). Albert Einstein expressed similar sentiments: "The most incomprehensible thing about the world is that it is comprehensible" (quoted in McGovern 2005:301).

Christian theology provides a simple but elegant answer to this question. Science works well because its foundational assumptions are true, rooted in the biblical doctrine of creation. Consider two of these assumptions. First, scientists assume that the universe has been put together and continues to behave in an orderly manner. We assume that carbon atoms have the same properties on earth and in stars and that gravity works the same way today that it did in the past. This assumption, which allows us to gain useful knowledge about nature even though we investigate only a tiny fraction of it, can never be directly demonstrated from within science. However, it grows naturally from the biblical teaching that an all-wise, rational God created the heavens and the earth (Pearcey and Thaxton 1994:24–27).

A second and equally critical assumption necessary for science is that humans have the mental capacity to recognize and understand this order in nature. We can figure out that order, even though it may be hidden from everyday view. Again, the biblical doctrine of creation gives us reason to believe that this assumption is true because God made humans in His image (Genesis 1:27). The Bible does not precisely define what it is about humans that represents God's image, but one common view is that God is reflected, at least in part, in the human capacity to think and choose freely (Erickson 1985:513), a capacity dependent on complex, creative, and rational thought—the key human elements necessary for science.

This interpretation—that biblical beliefs undergird the essential assumptions of science—may have been important in the history of science. For example, Melvin Calvin, recipient of a Nobel Prize in Chemistry for working out detailed biochemical pathways in photosynthesis, believed that the assumption of nature's orderliness could be traced historically to the ancient Hebrew view "that the universe is governed by a single God, and is not the product of the whims of many gods, each governing his own province according to his own laws" (1969:258). This interpretation suggests that biblical faith played a crucial role in the rise of modern science, although other intellectual strands (notably Greek philosophy) were also important.

## *The Limits of Science*

Although science has shown great power, it also has limits. Several Adventist scholars have addressed these limits in broad and helpful ways, and the reader is invited to consult their discussions for elaboration (e.g., Roth 1998:285–295; Brand 2009:16–39). Here, I will distill these limits into two categories: limitations of method that arise because fallible humans do science, and limits in scope that apply because reality extends beyond the subject matter of science. I will argue that Christian beliefs about creation and humankind help us make sense of both types of limits.

Science is a human endeavor, and all aspects of science are affected by this truth. This fact does not surprise Adventist biologists. Humans are finite creatures by creation (made in God's image—but never gods), fallen and selfish due to rebellion against God (Genesis 3:1–12), and thus thoroughly fallible in all we think and do—including our science. Occasionally, scientists display human fallibility in a reprehensible quest for self-gratification. High-profile cases of biomedical scientists who used fraudulent data to promote their research careers (Couzin 2006) serve as stark reminders of human sinfulness, although such breaches of ethics are by no means restricted to science. More commonly, our fallible human nature plays out in more subtle ways.

Let us begin with the collection of data. Good scientists attempt to collect data with care—to record observations and the results of experiments accurately and objectively. However, scientists almost always collect data for a purpose—they have a theory or hypothesis to test or a question to answer—and they often have preexisting ideas about where to look to find the relevant data, and what that data should look like. Such motivations and background expectations are essential to science because they undergird the persistence and focus necessary for effective scientific inquiry. However, they sometimes blind us—at least temporarily—to more relevant observations.

Here is a personal example. For many years, I wanted to know if the metabolic slowdown that occurs during the hibernation of modern ground squirrels leaves a recognizable mark in their teeth that could be detected if the teeth were preserved as fossils. Based on background reading, I developed expectations about what to look for and invested about 6 months of intense research on the question. The project failed;

the data I collected didn't answer the question, and I moved to other topics. About 5 years later, I came across a paper that spawned a new idea about what to look for. On a whim, I spent about 30 minutes testing this idea on some fossils I had on hand. And there it was—a clear abnormality in tooth structure, detectable in fossils, which might reflect hibernation! This discovery, taking only 30 minutes, launched a new research project, and we demonstrated convincingly that hibernation is reflected in the tooth structure of ground squirrels (Goodwin et al. 2005). The evidence had been there all along—I just didn't know what to look for until I had developed new expectations.

If the human element reveals itself in data collection, it does so even more in the creation of scientific theories and the operation of shaping principles. Philosophers of science remind us that theory formation doesn't flow simply or automatically from data. Rather, theories represent *ideas* creatively formed by human minds, and their formation and testing inevitably are shaped by our background beliefs and commitments—our shaping principles (Ratzsch 2000:18–20).

Consider Darwin's theory of evolution by natural selection. He developed this theory to make sense of much of the data that he had assembled, so data played an important role. However, his ideas also were shaped by the economic and philosophical ideas of his culture. Darwin's insight into the struggle for existence that results from overpopulation and limited resources in nature was attributed to Thomas Malthus, whose essay engaged these questions as they pertained to human economies. Furthermore, Darwin's uncompromising commitment to mechanistic explanations for the origin of species that did not involve divine action reflected a trend in philosophical thought at that time (Gillespie 1979). Thus, Darwin's theory represents a human construct whose origin was shaped not only by data, but also by background knowledge and metaphysical commitments.

This commitment to natural, mechanistic explanations in science deserves further comment. In one sense, this commitment is central to the scientific enterprise because it motivates scientists to probe unknown phenomena until they are well understood; we don't want scientists to invoke a divine miracle every time a phenomenon remains unexplained! Taken as a philosophical imperative, however, this commitment may restrict the range of plausible hypotheses considered for testing, especially in the historical sciences; recall the role that multiple, competing hypotheses play in these disciplines (Cleland 2001). As an example, a philosophical commitment to naturalism automatically excludes special creation as a hypothesis for the origin of life and biological design—regardless of whether scientific evidence might favor that hypothesis. (Earl Aagaard explores this theme at length in chapter 8.)

What does all this mean, practically, to the Adventist biologist who encounters apparently well-grounded scientific theories that conflict with our understanding of the Bible? Opinions vary. David Read, an Adventist attorney who has written a book on dinosaurs and the fossil record, argues that many current theories about life's history are so thoroughly molded by atheistic shaping principles that they must be rejected as false (2009). In this view, erroneous shaping principles drive formation of these theories; data play a secondary role.

Shandelle Henson, an Adventist mathematical ecologist, offers a differing perspective. She argues that the methods of science, although inevitably human and therefore fallible, represent a powerful way to keep subjective bias in check because of the ongoing interaction between data and scientific reasoning, and the careful scrutiny of scientific research by peer reviewers before it can be published (Henson 2009). In this view, data play a central role in keeping scientific ideas on track.

My own view is that we should always be aware of human fallibility when evaluating scientific theories, especially some theories pertaining to life's history that may be difficult to test in rigorous ways. Sometimes dominant shaping principles may play an inordinate role in guiding theory formation and testing. A classic example is the way Charles Lyell's commitment to interpret geology solely in terms of slow, gradual processes subsequently hampered advances in that discipline for decades (Gould 1984). Such metaphysical commitments, when broadly shared by a scientific community, hamper peer review because they lead scientists to exclude testable ideas without considering their empirical merit. However, over time, nature reveals its secrets to those who study it with patience. Even longstanding biases may be overcome—especially when scientists with diverse backgrounds and expectations address common problems, helping to counteract the blinding effect of individual biases. Practiced carefully, then, I see science as a thoroughly human (and thus fallible) but truth-tending way to learn about God's creation.

Let us now consider the second way in which science has limits: it is limited in the scope of its subject. Science offers powerful tools that help us describe and explain phenomena of the empirical universe. For the Christian, however, reality is both infinitely wider and much richer than the stuff of the universe, and science tells us little about these dimensions of reality. For starters, God—not the material universe—is the ultimate reality in the biblical worldview. Science offers a few hints about His character and work insofar as these are reflected in the natural world (Romans 1:20), but it can never reveal the depths of His character or the plans He has for the world as revealed through Jesus Christ. Only God's self-revelation gives us these insights.

Furthermore, human experience displays rich dimensions not fully reducible to the material level. We have deep convictions about right and wrong, often sense that our lives have meaning and purpose, and experience transcendence and beauty in nature, our relationships, and art. For the believer, these experiences reflect dimensions of created reality. God created the moral law to govern human conduct (Psalm 19:7–11) and formed humans with a basic moral orientation. He invested humans with purpose and meaning at creation (Genesis 1:26–27) and continues to do so across generations (Psalm 139:14–17). Again, science tells us little about these dimensions of reality.

Some scientists strongly disagree with this interpretation. In their view, science does explain our sense of morality, purpose, and so on—as evolutionary adaptations to improve human fitness. However, I concur with Del Ratzsch (1996:96–99), who argues that all such so-called explanations only work when what is to be explained is reduced to something less than it really is. As an example, science might "explain" our moral convictions as an adaptively useful tool to get us to behave in ways that maximize our fitness. (If my actions foster group bonding, for example, members of my group are more likely to help me when I need it, and I will have improved chances of success in raising kids who will pass on my genes.) However, this does not explain morality. It may explain why certain behaviors are useful but does not help us understand why we *ought* to act in moral ways—the real question of morality.

Finally, science faces limitations in scope even in the study of its proper domain: the material universe. Science often works well when asking questions about what things are made of, how they are put together, how natural phenomena work, when and where natural phenomena occur, and so on. These questions often begin with what, when, where, and how. Science falls silent, however, when we address ultimate questions about nature—questions that begin with a philosophical why. Why is the universe put together in precisely the right way to support intelligent life? Science does not tell us. Why does the universe exist at all? Again, science does not tell us. As believers, we obtain insight into these questions through God's Word.

To summarize, biblical teachings about God and humankind give perspective to science as a way of knowing. We have theological reasons to expect science to work well as a tool to understand the material universe that God made, and equally good reasons to expect science to have limits—a dual recognition that yields philosophical and practical implications for Adventist biologists. Philosophically, we should engage scientific ideas seriously but critically as we develop our own views about God and His creation. To apply a Bible passage in a modern dilemma, "[E]xamine everything carefully; hold fast to that which is good"[2] (1 Thessalonians 5:21). Practically, we do well to apply the demonstrated power of science to relieve suffering, improve quality of life, and carry out our role as stewards of creation—always remembering that, in our fallibility, these applications may bring unintended consequences. The discovery and widespread use of antibiotics have saved millions of lives—and have bred superbugs that become harder and harder to combat. Widespread application of artificial fertilizers has dramatically increased crop yields—and has resulted in soil degradation and increased water pollution. Science, applied wisely, has much power for good, but it will never be our savior.

## Viewing Science as a Means of Enriching Adventist Belief and Practice

In the preceding section, I argued that core Christian beliefs shared by Seventh-day Adventists (notably the doctrines of Creation and the Fall) provide a robust framework for understanding the power and limits of science as a human way to understand the natural world. We now turn to the second claim of this essay: that discoveries of science often enrich our beliefs and practices as Seventh-day Adventists.

---

2. All scripture quotations (unless otherwise noted) are taken from the NEW AMERICAN STANDARD BIBLE®, Copyright © 1960,1962,1963,1968,1971,1972, 1973,1975,1977,1995 by The Lockman Foundation. Used by permission.

## *God as Creator and Sustainer of Heaven and Earth*

Seventh-day Adventists fundamental belief 3 states, in part, "God the eternal Father is the Creator, Source, Sustainer, and Sovereign of all creation" (General Conference of Seventh-day Adventists 2005). A number of scientific discoveries, when viewed through the lens of faith, offer support for this belief because they suggest that important features of the universe, and of life on earth, reflect the clear intention and planning of a wise Creator. Biologists who advocate design in nature are struck by the highly integrated, tightly regulated, complex biochemical systems universal to living cells. They see no viable naturalistic explanation for how such systems could evolve through unguided natural processes, and they thus see evidence for divine design (e.g., Behe 1996; Brand 2009; chapters 2, 4, and 6 of this book).

As Adventist physicist Gary Burdick points out, however, profound design also may be displayed by what science has explained (2008). He recounts the story of how physicists came to understand the way the elements carbon and oxygen could be formed in the nuclear furnaces of stars. In doing so, they determined that both elements could only be formed, and in the right proportions to support life, if each element exhibited an excited state at a very precise energy level. Subsequent discoveries demonstrated that carbon and oxygen exhibit these precise excited states, and scientists were left to wonder, *Why?* Why is the universe put together in precisely the correct way to make this process which is so essential to life—all life on Earth needs carbon and oxygen, after all—work so optimally? The believer sensibly sees this as evidence for divine design.

Some Christians conclude that scientific evidence essentially compels belief in a Creator-God. Ariel Roth, a long-term contributor to Adventist thought on faith and science, offers this perspective in his illuminating book *Science Discovers God*, which reviews evidence for design from cosmology, chemistry, and biology. "The data of science itself is essentially forcing us to conclude that something unusual is going on," argues Roth, "and it looks as if a knowledgeable and transcendent God was involved in creating the complexities that scientific observation keeps uncovering" (2008:10). Other believers find such evidence suggestive but not coercive. After reviewing the astonishing rational beauty of nature and the exquisite fine-tuning of the universe to support conscious life, John Polkinghorne, a physicist who became an Anglican priest, concludes that a theistic interpretation of the universe, although not "logically coercive," offers an "intellectually satisfying understanding of what would otherwise be unintelligible good fortune" (1998:10). In either view, knowledge gained from science often is congruent with the Christian conviction that the universe is God's creation.

Science likewise informs how we understand God's role through Christ as Sustainer of all creation. Bible writers attribute many processes in the natural world to God's action: growth of plants and sustenance of animal life (Psalm 147:8–9), weather and wind (Psalm 147:16–18), and human development (Psalm 139:13), to name a few. However, as Frank Marsh correctly notes, the Bible says "nothing about *how* God accomplishes" the work of sustaining creation, and so "[His] method of operation is left for man to discover" (1947:65). In this light, the findings of science suggest that God ordinarily cares for His creation by upholding the governing natural laws that He put in place (a theme that David Cowles explores in chapter 6).

Perhaps the most important contribution that scientific study makes to our belief in God is that it gives practical occasion to live out this belief—to "worship Him who made the heaven and the earth and sea and springs of waters" (Revelation 14:7). Many scientists—even those without religious orientation—express amazement and awe at the grandeur and complexity of what they study, and they sometimes express this experience in transcendent, almost religious terms (e.g., Wilson 2006:55–61). Christian biologists can take this experience a step further. With Job of long ago, confronted by God's power manifest in untamed nature (Job 39–41), we are reminded of our smallness, repent of our prideful ways, and worship our Creator (Job 42:1–6).

Although the study of nature provides insights into Christian beliefs about God, we must acknowledge that it does so with complexity and ambiguity. I recall one magical Friday evening in south Florida, when students marveled with their teachers at the exquisite behavior of an orb-weaving spider constructing its web. Some mentioned this marvel of design in worship reflections later that evening. Sabbath morning, however, one thoughtful student pointed out that this beautiful web serves as a death trap and mused about its meaning. Nature is full of such twists, which complicate simple design-of-nature arguments for God's existence. In a fallen world we see through a glass darkly.

### *Adventist Conception of Humankind*

The Genesis narrative tells us, "[T]he Lord God formed man of dust from the ground, and breathed into his nostrils the breath of life; and man became a living being" (2:7). This narrative grounds two truths about human nature. First, we share much with the rest of creation because we are made of the same material (birds and beasts also were formed "out of the ground"—Genesis 2:19). Second, our status as "living souls" reflects an indivisible unity between body and spirit. Seventh-day Adventists have formalized the last truth in fundamental belief 7 which states, in part, that "[Each person] is an indivisible unity of body, mind, and spirit, dependent upon God for life and breath and all else" (General Conference of Seventh-day Adventists 2005). The Seventh-day Adventist commitment to wholesome and healthful living flows from these convictions: if I am to care for my soul, I must care for my whole being—body, mind, and spirit.

Scientific discoveries continue to illuminate these beliefs and commitments. Biochemistry shows us that we share much of the fundamental molecular machinery of life with other creatures, and ecology reveals the critical ways that humans are integrated into natural ecosystems. On a practical level, advancing knowledge in nutrition and wellness confirms Adventist commitments to healthful living (e.g., Fraser 1999). More theoretically, scientific discoveries give insight into the wholeness of human nature. We still have much to learn in this arena. (See chapter 3, in which Karl Bailey explores how scientific knowledge sheds light on our belief that human consciousness represents a body-mind unity.)

## Accepting That Adventist Beliefs and Scientific Discovery Sometimes Challenge Each Other

Up to this point, I have emphasized the positive ways that Seventh-day Adventist beliefs and science interact. We must acknowledge, however, that for Seventh-day Adventists, biblical beliefs and scientific knowledge sometimes challenge each other. We experience this challenge most directly when we study the history of life. Adventists accept the creation narratives of Genesis as factual history (e.g., Davidson 2003), describing God's work of creation in six real days followed by the Sabbath (fundamental belief 6, in part; General Conference of Seventh-day Adventists 2005). Modern scientific discoveries are interpreted to indicate a process of gradual formation over a very long period of time. How do we bring the evidence from the Bible and nature into a coherent picture of creation?

Subsequent essays will explore Adventist responses to specific challenges from evolutionary theory (chapter 4) and the study of fossils (chapter 5). Here, we will consider four general principles for constructive dialogue that will affirm the authority of the Bible, encourage growth in our understanding of both the Bible and nature, and facilitate respectful conversations among participants.[3]

First, we must affirm the authority of the scriptures and not force interpretations of the Bible to accommodate science. For example, some believers have interpreted the days of Genesis 1 as figurative, representing indefinite periods of creation (e.g., Ross 2004). This interpretation helps resolve the time-discrepancy between geology and Genesis, but Adventist scholars have rejected it because it is inconsistent with evidence in the biblical text (Hasel 1994; Davidson 2003).

Second, we must be honest with the empirical evidence of science and not force interpretations of this evidence to resolve tensions. As believers, we naturally wish to harmonize what we learn from nature and the Bible—God's two books. However, we must do science carefully, only taking our scientific conclusions as far as evidence allows, and honestly publish these conclusions—even when what we discover does not meet our expectations. Adventist archaeologists are known and respected for modeling this approach in their discipline (Younker 2004).

Third, we need to seek integration. Although biblical and scientific studies have their own methods of investigation and testing, there is an appropriate way for the two to dialogue when they disagree: each may encourage the other to reexamine long-held interpretations and consider alternatives. In some cases, scientific ideas have helped believers identify faulty biblical interpretation (for example, the claim that the Bible advocates a geocentric universe). In other cases, biblical concepts have suggested new lines of scientific inquiry, leading to discoveries that reduce the tension between scientific theories and our understanding of the Bible (see chapter 5 for examples).

3. I'm indebted to Ben Clausen for the basic ideas described in this section, and I am using these ideas with his permission. Clausen is a geophysicist at the Geoscience Research Institute, and he has been a long-term contributor to the science-faith dialogue.

Ideally, integration will eliminate conflict between our understanding of science and the Bible, but in practice some conflicts persist. Such conflicts can be deeply frustrating, but they shouldn't surprise us: all our knowledge is partial and subject to human frailty! Indeed, it is just these points of conflict that may suggest new lines of research and discovery. Also, knowing that we simply cannot and do not know everything tempers human ego, encourages humility, and fosters intellectual honesty. Thus, the presence of unresolved tension may serve not as the enemy, but as the servant to Christian faith: believers are encouraged to grow in both knowledge and character while remaining faithful to God's Word (Goodwin 2008).

Finally, we must be respectful in our dialogue with each other. The conversations about science and the Bible often are heated and angry, even among fellow Christians. Perhaps we will be more respectful and generous to each other when we remember our own frailty, and Christ's command to love one another—even as we vigorously debate how to harmonize God's His Word and the world that He created.

## Outlining the Plan for This Book

Science and Christian belief, then, can be considered honest friends. Christian belief provides a framework for understanding science as a way of knowing; scientific discoveries shed light on biblical beliefs about God and humanity; and the two sometimes challenge each other to find better explanations.

The remainder of the book will explore this honest friendship across a range of biological topics. Chapters 2 and 3 relate to the broad question "Who are we?" They explore how scientific discoveries in genomics and human cognition relate to Adventist beliefs. Chapters 4 and 5 pertain to the question of origins: "Where did we come from?" One chapter explores the scope and limits of evolution, and the other reflects on how Adventists have understood the fossil record. Chapters 6 and 7 bear on the question "What is our place in the world?" One contribution engages ecology from a philosophical perspective; the other calls us to practically take up our first calling given by God: to be good stewards of creation. Chapter 8 will draw from themes developed in the book and offer perspectives on the roles of definitions, bias (especially as driven by worldview), and Intelligent Design in the science-faith discussion. Finally, the epilogue invites you, as reader, to reflect on how the dialogue between biology and

Adventist faith may inform and shape your life—no matter the career pathway you may choose or are currently engaged in.

The authors of this book represent numerous specialties within biology and hail from five Seventh-day Adventist colleges or universities and one research institute. Despite our diverse backgrounds and perspectives (we will not agree with each other about some things!), we share several deep commitments: a love for biology, a passion for our faith, and the desire to live meaningful lives that integrate the two. Our goal in this book is to flesh out these commitments and to encourage you, the reader, to join us in the lifelong adventure of thinking—and living—as Seventh-day Adventist students of God's creation.

Enjoy the journey!

## Literature Cited

Behe, M. J. 1996. Darwin's black box: The biochemical challenge to evolution. Free Press, New York.

Brand, L. R. 2009. Faith, reason, and earth history, 2nd ed. Andrews University Press, Berrien Springs, Michigan.

Burdick, G. 2008. Science and design: A physicist's perspective. Dialogue 20(3):5–7.

Calvin, M. 1969. Chemical evolution. Oxford University Press, New York and Oxford.

Cleland, C. E. 2001. Historical science, experimental science, and the scientific method. Geology 29:987–990.

Couzin, J. 2006. Breakdown of the year: Scientific fraud. Science 314:1853.

Davidson, R. M. 2003. The biblical account of origins. Journal of the Adventist Theological Society 14:4–43.

Erickson, M. J. 1985. Christian theology, one volume ed. Baker Book House, Grand Rapids, Michigan.

Fraser, G. E. 1999. Association between diet and cancer, ischemic heart disease, and all-cause mortality in non-Hispanic white Californian Seventh-day Adventists. American Journal of Clinical Nutrition 70:532s–538s.

General Conference of Seventh-day Adventists. 2005. Fundamental beliefs. Accessed 1/4/10 at: http://www.adventist.org/beliefs/fundamental/index.html.

Gillespie, N. C. 1979. Charles Darwin and the problem of creation. University of Chicago Press, Chicago.

Goodwin, H. T. 2008. When faith and knowledge clash: Leveraging the tension to advance Christian education. The Journal of Adventist Education 70(4):44–47.

Goodwin, H. T., G. R. Michener, D. Gonzalez, and C. E. Rinaldi. 2005. Hibernation is recorded in lower incisors of recent and fossil ground squirrels (*spermophilus*). Journal of Mammalogy 86:323–332.

Gould, S. J. 1984. Toward the vindication of punctuational change. Pp. 9–34 in Catastrophes and earth history: The new uniformitarianism (W. A. Berggren and J. A. Van Couvering, eds.). Princeton University Press, Princeton, New Jersey.

Hasel, G. F. 1994. The "days" of creation in Genesis 1: Literal "days" or figurative "periods/epochs" of time? Origins 21:5–38.

Henson, S. M. 2009. Why mathematics, science, and humanities (including religion) don't have a quarrel. Spectrum 37(3):44–49.

Kuhn, T. S. 1970. The structure of scientific revolutions, 2nd ed. University of Chicago Press, Chicago.

Marsh, F. L. 1947. Evolution, creation, and science, 2nd ed. Review and Herald Publishing Association, Washington, DC.

McGovern, U., ed. 2005. Webster's new world dictionary of quotations. Wiley, New York.

Pearcey, N., and C. Thaxton. 1994. The soul of science: Christian faith and natural philosophy. Crossway Books, Wheaton, Illinois.

Polkinghorne, J. 1998. Belief in God in an age of science. Yale University Press, New Haven, Connecticut.

Ratzsch, D. 1996. The battle of beginnings: Why neither side is winning the creation-evolution debate. InterVarsity Press, Downers Grove, Illinois.

Ratzsch, D. 2000. Science and its limits: The natural sciences in Christian perspective. InterVarsity Press, Downers Grove, Illinois.

Read, D. C. 2009. Dinosaurs: An Adventist view. Clarion Call Books, Keene, Texas.

Ross, H. 2004. A matter of days: Resolving a creation controversy. Navpress, Colorado Springs, Colorado.

Roth, A. A. 1998. Origins: Linking science and scripture. Review and Herald Publishing Association, Hagerstown, Maryland.

Roth, A. A. 2008. Science discovers God: Seven convincing lines of evidence for His existence. Review and Herald Publishing Association, Hagerstown, Maryland.

Wigner, E. 1960. The unreasonable effectiveness of mathematics in the natural sciences. Communication in Pure and Applied Mathematics 13:1–14.

Wilson, E. O. 2006. The creation: An appeal to save life on earth. W. W. Norton, New York.

Younker, R. W. 2004. Integrating faith, the Bible, and archaeology: A review of the "Andrews University way" of doing archaeology. Pp. 43–52 in The Future of Biblical Archaeology: Reassessing Methodologies and Assumptions (J. K. Hoffmeier and A. Millard, eds.). Wm. B. Eerdmans, Grand Rapids, Michigan.

# Chapter Two

# GENOMES: WHAT THEY TELL US ABOUT LIFE, SCIENCE, AND GOD

**Timothy G. Standish**

On Thursday, February 15, 2001, I taught my molecular genetics class at Andrews University how to estimate the number of genes in the human genome—or so I thought at the time. The available data were sound, and the logic I used to interpret these data made sense. Humans definitely had about 125,000 genes...until I awoke the next morning to discover that we don't have even half that many.

The actual number of human genes had not changed overnight, but publication of the human genome profoundly changed our understanding of several things previously thought true—including how many genes we have. Abundant new data made previous logic and reasonable inferences irrelevant. This event probably did nothing to build my students' confidence in the "hard sciences," but that may not have been a bad thing. In fact, the most valuable lesson any science student can learn is how tentative scientific theories are. At any time, even the most well-established theory may prove to be completely wrong, no matter how clever and certain it seems. Science routinely surprises us because theories are always subject to empirical data, and new data continually accrue. These surprises are exciting to individuals willing to enjoy them, but ever-changing science may frustrate dogmatists who insist that it conform to their opinions.

## Exploring Genomes: Attributes and Origin

Current genome data reveal remarkable information about life that has amazed, surprised, and, sometimes humbled biologists. But what exactly is a genome? A genome comprises all of the genetic material in an organism, with the possible exception of viral DNA that may reside in some cells. The human genome includes all DNA packaged into the 23 human chromosomes, two copies of which are found in most cells, as well as DNA within mitochondria. While genomes display remarkable chemical structure, what really counts is their capacity to encode information. The nucleic acid language of DNA stores information far more efficiently than printed words on paper. For example, human mitochondrial DNA is only about 5.6 μm long—about one hundredth the diameter of a typical period at the end of a sentence—but printed out, its DNA sequence takes up about 6 pages. Similarly, the entire human genome is about a meter long but requires about a million pages to print out!

The fact that genomes are information generates important practical and ethical questions for the Christian biologist. Who owns the information? How can or should it be used? And what might constitute appropriate manipulation of genomic information? Keep these questions in mind as you read the rest of this chapter, and we will return to them at the end. However, first we need to discuss the origin of genetic information, a topic that will inform everything else in our discussion.

### *What are the Origins of Genomic Information?*

Christians believe God created living things and is the ultimate source of information in genomes. In contrast, the most common alternative theory of origins—materialistic Darwinism—attributes genomic information to chance mutations and natural laws, particularly natural selection. This chapter may not provide a definitive answer to the origins question for most readers, but understanding genomes does provide a useful basis for making an informed decision. So let's look at several attributes of genomes that shed light on the origin of genomes and ultimately of life. We will then return to important ethical and practical questions raised by the study of genomes.

### *Is the Genome Really Information Dense?*

Genomics has demonstrated that organisms, like the cells that compose them, are more than collections of matter—they are rich collections of *information.* The Bible does not compel Christians to believe that *all* DNA encodes functional information, just as Darwinism does not compel its adherents to believe that only a fraction of DNA is functional (Standish 2002). However, Christian theism and Darwinism provide a general difference in expectations. Christians expect that, when studied carefully, the fallen creation will still reveal some of its original beauty, whereas many Darwinists have a very different perspective. Susumu Ohno, who coined the term "junk DNA," elegantly expressed this viewpoint: "[T]he earth is strewn with fossil remains of extinct species; is it a wonder that our genome too is filled with the remains of extinct genes?" (1972:80)

Unfortunately, our understanding of genomes was held back by the rush to declare many genomes "junk" (Makalowski 2003). Much DNA does not code for proteins, and many biologists initially assumed that these noncoding DNA sequences therefore lacked function. The logic boiled down to "If we don't know what it does, it must do nothing." However, significant data now demonstrates that this logic is false: noncoding DNA often exhibits important functions. This understanding has revolutionized how biologists view genomes. Instead of vast deserts with occasional oases of functional information, genomes now seem more like rainforests of information with a dazzling array of genes, control mechanisms, logic circuits, and other functions waiting to be discovered.

### *Is Functional DNA Conserved DNA?*

As noted above, genome scientists have discovered that much noncoding DNA really has function, but they also have discovered that some DNA thought to be functional may be disposable. Scientists screen for probable functional sequences by looking for conserved DNA—that is, DNA that differs little from species to species—because functional sequences should be subject to stabilizing natural selection. However, recent discoveries complicate this picture. Segments as large as 1.6 million bases can be removed from the mouse genome with no apparent effect—even though the deleted segment contains highly conserved regions of DNA that are identical among rats, mice, and humans (Pagán Westphal 2004; Ahituv et al. 2007). If humans are separated from mice and rats by tens of millions of years of evolution, why have these apparently disposable segments been maintained by natural selection? Are disposable segments really functionless? Was it really natural selection that maintained these disposable segments? If not, a more recent origin for these species provides one possible explanation, but the mystery remains. Perhaps the answer will surprise everyone, Christian and Darwinist alike! What this example and others show is that assumptions about what is functional in genomes and what is not have proven unreliable up to this point; even assumptions that sound reasonable should be viewed with caution.

## *Are Genes What We Thought They Were?*

During my education, biologists worked with a relatively simple understanding of the gene. According to the "one gene, one enzyme" hypothesis proposed by Beadle and Tatum (for which they won a Nobel Prize), each gene codes for a single protein; but now everything has changed. Current estimates indicate that humans have fewer than 25,000 genes but produce more than 100,000 proteins (Clamp et al. 2007), thus at least some genes must be capable of producing multiple proteins.

How is this achieved? Let's illustrate with the human Paired-like Homeodomain Transcription Factor 2 gene (also called Pituitary Homeobox 2 and abbreviated *Pitx2*), which shows how RNA processing creates several different proteins from one gene. The *Pitx2* protein plays a role in development of the head and eyes, among other things (Gage et al. 1999). *Pitx2* includes six exons separated by five introns (Fig. 1). By joining exons 1, 2, 5 and 6, RNA processing creates the mRNA for a version of *Pitx2* called Isoform A, or *Pitx2A*. Joining exons 1, 2, 3, 5, and 6 makes mRNA for *Pitx2B* and exons 4, 5, and 6 form the mRNA for *Pitx2C*. Further variations in the protein products of this gene are achieved using different translation start sites on the mRNA as well as other differences in RNA splicing (Lamba et al. 2008). Changing parts of the protein presumably impacts how *Pitx2* interacts with other molecules, thus cells need to make the right "version" of *Pitx2* in the right place at the right time if the organism they are part of is to develop normally.

This raises a profound question: How does the cell "know" when to join (splice in genetic terminology) certain exons but not others? This brings us back to some of what was once dismissed as "junk" DNA and indicates why genomes are now understood to be far more dynamic than initially imagined. The complex systems controlling exon splicing appear to involve sequences occupying at least one third of the human genome (Zhang et al. 2008), far exceeding the 3% of the human genome thought to be functional a few years ago. Furthermore, small RNA transcripts may participate in regulating many other steps in protein production. Indeed, at least 70% of the genome is transcribed as RNA (Pheasant and Mattick 2007), commonly including both strands of the DNA molecule—not just the strand that codes for protein (RIKEN Genome Exploration Research Group and Genome Science Group [Genome Network Project Core Group] and the FANTOM Consortium 2005). A

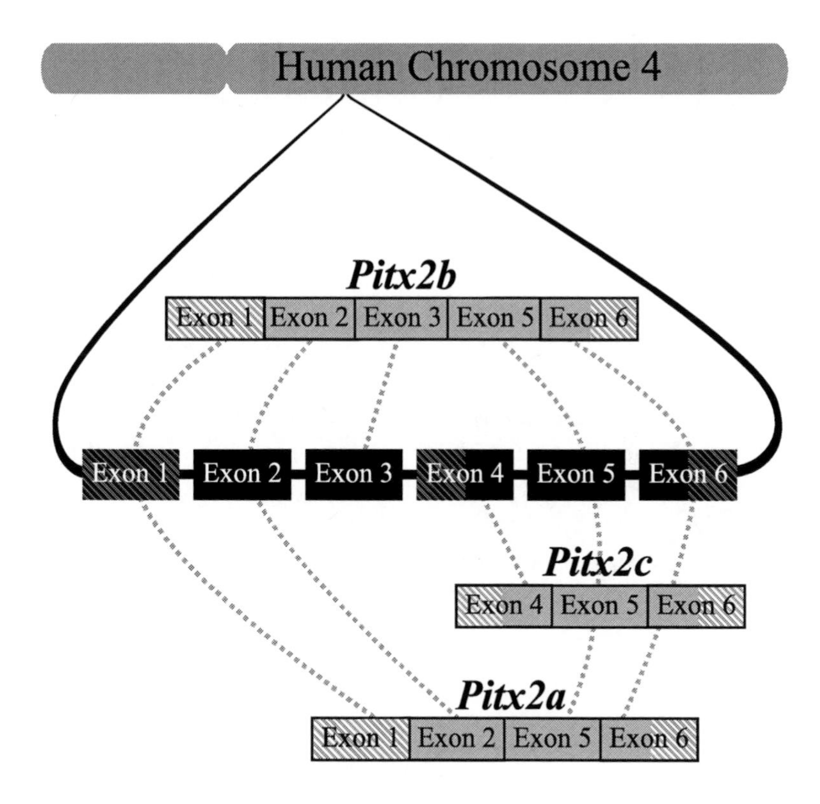


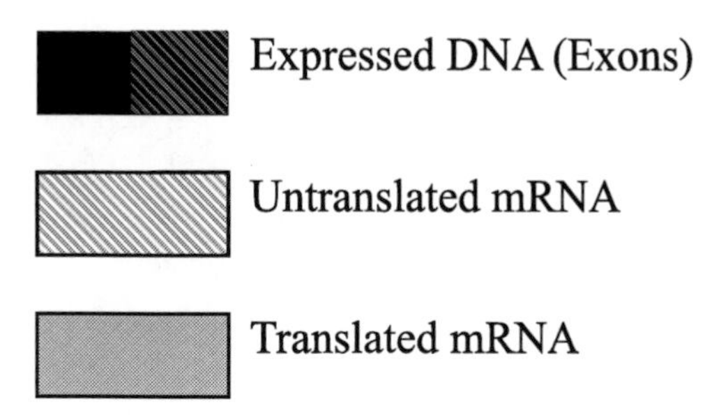


**Figure 1**—The human *Pitx2* gene composed of 6 exons separated by 5 introns. Splicing (joining) different exons creates different proteins from this single gene. Exons and introns not drawn to scale. Unique mRNAs shown for *PITX2A*, B, and C after processing to remove introns and other RNA.

Christian who believes God wrote the first genomes might be particularly motivated to investigate what all the RNA transcripts are doing.

### *What Do "Broken" Genes Tell Us?*

Biologists have identified numerous sequences in the genome, which they interpret as *pseudogenes*—copies of genes that appear to have crippling mutations that would eradicate their normal function. Pseudogenes seemed to be prime examples of so-called junk DNA, and such sequences, when shared across species, are still often invoked as strong evidence for common ancestry. However, some of these pseudogenes have been found to be involved with essential functions. For example, one pseudogene appears to be essential for egg formation in mice (Tam et al. 2008). Perhaps more startling has been the discovery that other pseudogenes play an important regulatory role. Disruption of this regulation can, in at least one case, lead to cancer (Poliseno et al. 2010). The possibility that regulatory functions may be a widespread characteristic of pseudogenes prompted one scientist to state:

> This means that not only have we discovered a new language for mRNA, but we have also translated the previously unknown language of up to 17,000 pseudogenes and at least 10,000 long non-coding (lnc) RNAs. Consequently, we now know the function of an estimated 30,000 new entities, offering a novel dimension by which cellular and tumor biology can be regulated, and effectively doubling the size of the functional genome. (Pandolfi 2010)

Discovery of functional pseudogenes was not anticipated by most scientists and shows how much we still have to learn. If certain pseudogenes are not really broken genes but rather important functional components of genomes, this may call into question elements in the logic used when invoking pseudogenes and other "junk" DNA as evidence for common ancestry.

Revisions in our understanding of how genomes work reveal an awe-inspiring level of sophistication in their design. It turns out that control mechanisms encoded in at least some pseudogenes and other "junk DNA" are as important as the genes they regulate and that humans, along with all other living things, really are "fearfully and wonderfully made"[1] (Psalm 139:14). The Christian worldview encourages believers to see the sublime beauty evident in genomes and the rest of creation while still acknowledging that the creation is profoundly broken and in need of restoration.

### *What Is the Origin of Gene Families?*

The fewer than 25,000 genes currently estimated in the human genome barely surpass the number present in the tiny, 1 mm-long nematode worms (*Caenorhabditis elegans*) I studied for my PhD, but in one sense even this estimate may be high. Many genes—possibly more than half of the genes in the human genome—come in families that code for clearly related proteins.

Biologists have developed a model for how gene families evolve—through gene duplication followed by divergence of separate copies over time (e.g., Lodish et al. 1995:313–314)—but genomic information may complicate this simple model. For example, globin proteins share similarities but have specialized roles as they modulate the affinity of hemoglobin for oxygen during development. The globin genes are arranged neatly on chromosomes *in their order of expression.* Well-ordered systems such as this are known as products of careful effort, but their creation through unguided Darwinian mechanisms seems more than can be reasonably expected.

### *Why Are Genes Found in Unexpected Places?*

Genes sometimes show up in unexpected places. For example poly-γ-glutamate (PGA) synthase represents a multipart protein that seems to be essential for jellyfish stings to work. Curiously, one subunit of this protein closely resembles a protein found in bacteria (Denker et al. 2008)! Darwinists explain this observation by invoking Horizontal Gene Transfer (HGT, also called Lateral Gene Transfer): a bacterial gene was presumably transferred to the common ancestor of jellyfish and their relatives (*phylum Cnidaria*) and subsequently inherited by all cnidarians. However, this hypothesis faces challenges. Among other things, if a virus or some other vector transferred the gene, it must have been capable of packaging up bacterial DNA, entering a cnidarian germ-line cell, and integrating the DNA into the genome. The bacterial gene would have to survive and somehow acquire an appropriate

1. All Scripture quotations, unless otherwise noted, are taken from the King James Version.

control mechanism. The resultant offspring either had to be more fit due to the presence of the bacterial gene, or be incredibly lucky, so that the gene became fixed in the common ancestor of all cnidarians.

The HGT hypothesis postulates a kind of recombinant DNA technology, an activity that intelligent agents are capable of doing. Do we have evidence that it happens in nature without intelligent guidance? Yes, it appears to occur *among* bacteria, where a set of machinery does the work, but it is not clear whether it can happen spontaneously between bacteria and more complex multicelled eukaryotes, or between eukaryotes. Furthermore, even if HGT did take place between such taxa, it is not clear how the rest of the steps transpired to incorporate the inserted DNA into the essential machinery of the host—as is postulated to have occurred in jellyfish. On the other hand, intelligent molecular biologists routinely engineer organisms like this, but only with much thought and effort.

Christians may be tempted to conclude that all eukaryotic cases attributed to HGT are evidence of intelligent genome engineering by God. If so, the problem of evil arises. PGA synthase appears critical to the poison injectors in jellyfish. If God put this gene into jellyfish, is He responsible for the death and misery that result? That is a question I myself pondered after encountering a Portuguese Man o' War (*Physalia physalis*)—a most painful experience!

Although Christian biologists are free to conclude that HGT sometimes occurs, the mechanism is usually invoked to accommodate data contrary to a specific hypothesis of common ancestry. This may work in some cases such as bacteria, but this raises a problem when inferring common ancestry. Examination of genomes reveals that HGT profoundly complicates any logical inference of evolutionary history, particularly in bacteria. Gene A may be most similar to a gene in one species while gene B is closer to one in a completely different species. As long as only one gene is used, a reasonably clear evolutionary tree—phylogeny—may result, but analyzing a different gene may yield a significantly different phylogeny (Haggerty et al. 2009).

### *Sliced, Diced, and Blended Genomes?*

Several issues, including the prevalence of HGT, have led some scientists to doubt current Darwinian explanations for the origin of genomes. For example, Lynn Margulis believes that the genomes we see did not evolve by simple modification of DNA inherited from ancestors. Margulis and her son, Dorian Sagan, argue that living organisms are chimeras made up of blended genomes from several ancient organisms (2002). Carl Woese (2002) and others have expressed similar ideas (e.g., Williamson 1992, 2001; Sapp 1994). The genomes of bacteria reveal that Darwin's "tree of life" lacks roots and a trunk. Taken as a whole, no Last Universal Common Ancestor (LUCA) can be logically inferred from genomic data. Indeed, some Darwinists now claim there is no single tree of life and never was one: "[T]he tree of life, one of the iconic concepts of evolution, has turned out to be a figment of our imagination" (Lawton 2009). Of course, just because some Darwinists along with many Christians question the evidence for LUCA does not mean that all Darwinists are ready to abandon universal common ancestry. For example, Theobald (2010) gives a spirited statistical defense of the concept while also defining LUCA in a way that many would find surprising: "the last universal common ancestor may have comprised a population of organisms with different genotypes that lived in different places at different times."

### *Are Genome Comparisons Realistic?*

As described in the preceding section, HGT confounds phylogeny construction at the deepest levels: at the root and trunk of the hypothetical tree of life. However, the branches of this "tree," which unite relatively similar organisms, make more sense phylogenetically. In general, the genomes of organisms believed to be closely related based on morphology share more in common than do genomes of organisms exhibiting less morphological similarity. This observation is consistent with the hypothesis of shared ancestry but is also consistent with common design (see chapter 4). Irrespective of one's assumptions, it is not surprising that the instructions for making similar things are also similar—especially if they share a common designer. For example, I would not be surprised to discover that certain words, phrases, and even sentences in this chapter correspond to other papers I have written about similar topics. Perhaps immodestly, I hope readers will give me some credit for the product of my mind—and not conclude that all I write is the result of an unguided alteration of letters or paragraph rearrangements, followed by an unguided filtering process like natural selection!

Similarly, as a Christian biologist, when I compare diverse genomes I conclude that God used similar materials and "words" when He wrote out the information they contain. However, while there are profound similarities across many genomes, current evidence points to some startling differences that may complicate Darwinian interpretations. Let's turn our attention to some of these differences.

### *Are Some Genes "Orphans"?*

We have just examined *similar* genes across diverse genomes and how they may be interpreted: as resulting from common ancestry or horizontal gene transfer (in Darwinian models), or from shared design. In addition, genomic studies also reveal genes that are *unique* to individual taxa. These "orphan" genes comprise about 10–20% of genes in most species (Khalturin et al. 2009). Some of these genes may be artifacts of the algorithms used to locate genes in long DNA sequences, but many of them probably are unique and must have come from somewhere. Two Darwinian explanations might work to explain "orphan" genes: 1) the genes evolved uniquely in each taxon; or 2) the genes were present in the ancestral species and have been lost in all but one descendent of that ancestor. Creationists have no problem with the second explanation; it obviously is a lot easier to lose genes than it is to make them in the first place, and there is evidence that this happens.

For example, multiple, separate stickleback fish populations lack a regulatory sequence about 30 kb upstream from the *Pitx1* homeobox gene, and this seems to explain their greatly reduced dorsal spines and pelvic girdle (Chan et al. 2010). However, an organism must have a gene before it can lose it; Darwinists must still explain how the gene originated in the first place. Attributing the origin of genes to a Creator addresses this issue while acknowledging that genomes may well change in some ways as organisms adapt to their environment.

### *Why Do Some Parts of Genomes Have Greater Variation Than Others?*

The preceding section noted how genomes differ in the *genes* they contain, but genomes also differ in the DNA sequence of *shared* genes and chromosomes. Intriguingly, such differences appear to be nonrandom; they are more abundant in certain biological systems and even on certain chromosomes. For example, several genes known to play a role in development of the nervous system in chimps and humans vary more than is typical in comparisons between other genes shared by both species. Darwinists attribute this to "positive selection" on those genes (Ponting and Jackson 2005), but why this selection would operate on genes impacting human ancestors' intelligence and not that of chimpanzee ancestors is not obvious. It is hard to imagine that intelligence is adaptive in only humans and their ancestors.

On a larger scale, entire chromosomes differ to varying degrees. For example, chimps and humans show striking similarity in their X chromosome but greater differences between the other chromosomes—particularly the Y chromosome (Hughes et al. 2010). Positive selection might explain why some *genes* differ more than others between species, but it's not obvious to me how natural selection explains changes to the entire architecture of some *chromosomes* and not others. On the other hand, patterns analogous to those seen in genomes are common in books that are edited for different purposes by a single author or editor. During her lifetime Ellen G. White demonstrated a pattern like this in the packaging and repackaging of material she wrote into *Spiritual Gifts,* then *Spirit of Prophecy,* and finally *Conflict of the Ages.*

Darwinists have proposed complex explanations to account for the nonrandom distribution of differences between genomes. For example, to accommodate variation in chimp-human genome comparisons, Patterson and colleagues (2006) offered the following model: an ancestral lineage evolved into two species that occasionally exchanged genetic material over about 4 million years before finally separating about 6.3 million years ago (note that I'm not endorsing the idea of millions of years here). The complexity of a scenario like this, which seems to offer an *ad hoc* explanation for the nonrandom distribution of differences between the chimpanzee and human genomes, is not just unattractive to those who doubt that chimpanzees and humans share a common ancestor. Some scientists have suggested that promiscuity among chimpanzee females may be a more parsimonious explanation of the data (Dolgin 2009), but is this really a simpler explanation than accepting that humans and chimps do not share a common ancestor?

## *Why Are There Different Numbers of Chromosomes?*

One notable difference between human and chimpanzee genomes is the number of chromosomes: humans have 23 and chimpanzees have 24 chromosomes. On the face of it, this presents a problem that must be explained if both share a common ancestor. However, an examination of the banding pattern evident in chromosomes from both species suggests a possible answer. Human chromosome 2 reveals a striking resemblance to chimpanzee chromosomes designated 2a and 2b. Long before sophisticated DNA sequencing was available, this evidence was interpreted to mean that the two smaller chromosomes found in chimpanzees and other apes were present in the ancestor of humans and apes, and that these two fused to form human chromosome 2 (Yunis et al. 1980; Yunis and Prakash 1982).

Sequence data for human chromosome 2 further supports the occurrence of a fusion event. Distinctive structures called telomeres occupy the ends of each chromosome, and human chromosome 2 exhibits telomere-like DNA sequences in the region where the two ancestral chromosomes are thought to have fused (IJdo et al. 1991). Thus, the case for a chromosome fusion event that created human chromosome 2 seems reasonable, and some believers clearly accept the idea that chromosomes fused in the common ancestor of other organisms (e.g., Wood 2008). As an example, horses have 32 chromosomes while donkeys have 31. If they genuinely descended from a common ancestor, there must have been either a fusion event or a chromosome-splitting event. If chromosome fusion occurred for horse-like creatures, why not in the lineage of humans?

The question, however, is not whether genomes may have been rearranged in the past; rather, the question that Christians and materialists alike seek to answer is whether humans share a common ancestor with other organisms—with apes being the most obvious candidates. The chromosomal evidence does not compel belief in common ancestry because the hypothesized fusion event, if it happened, occurred *within* the human lineage. At best the chromosome-fusion theory allows human ancestors to share the same number of chromosomes as living apes, accommodating the data to the hypothesis of common ancestry; it is not logically evidence of common ancestry.

### *Do Adventists Believe Humans and Apes Share a Common Ancestor?*

It is easy to criticize materialist ideas about humanity's relationship with apes, but some published statements by Seventh-day Adventist writers are also disturbing. For example, Uriah Smith argued, in the *Review and Herald,* that "[N]aturalists affirm that the line of demarcation between the human and animal races is lost in confusion. It is impossible, as they affirm, to tell just where the human ends and the animal begins" (1866). Dores Robinson, secretary of Ellen G. White, expressed similar thoughts: "Anyone who observes the chimpanzee, the gorilla or the orang, would not find it difficult to believe that they have some common ancestry with the human race.... It is far more reasonable to believe that apes descended from man" (1931).

My personal observation is that similarities between human and chimpanzee genomes have been oversold and that the evidence ultimately does not support the claim of common ancestry between apes and humans. However, being a Christian does not compel much other than wonder when it comes to studying genomes. If similarities exist between humans and other creatures, Christians should not feel compelled to deny them; the same Creator made all life forms, with their similarities and differences. These similarities and differences should be expected in genomes. Darwinism imposes greater constraints on what is expected, and common ancestry requires some complex explanations of genome data. Liberated by our worldview to see creation as it is, Christians need not face a crisis of faith every time some data are consistent with Darwinian views. We do well to remember that worldviews may color how data are interpreted and that humans tend to oversell arguments that fit their worldviews.

To summarize, genomes display profound similarities—there is a deep unity to life, which at the molecular level speaks approximately the same language and shares a related set of genes. However, our models for how genomes originated must explain both profound similarities *and* profound differences. When investigators arbitrarily eliminate design from consideration, and impose common ancestry, molecular data suggest a complicated story of life best represented by a bush with many interconnecting twigs, rather than a tree with a single trunk and gradually branching taxonomic groups. Conversely, when investigators permit design as a legitimate scientific explanation, molecular data suggest a Designer who combined standard parts—genes—in novel ways to create different kinds of organisms. However, while much current genome data seem explicable within the Christian worldview, it is worth keeping in mind that tension, like the problem of evil, still exists and, if history is any guide, the science of genomics will continue to yield surprises no matter what one's worldview.

## Moving Beyond Genomes

At this point, I hope you see some of the wonder and mystery of genomes. They are beautiful, complex, elegantly efficient at encoding data, and yet remain mysterious with much yet to be learned about them! Some of what we know about genomes fits well with the thesis of common ancestry and Darwinian evolution, but when taken as a whole, I personally see the evidence as most consistent with the Christian worldview, especially the enormous quantities of information stored in genomes, the elegant arrangement of information, and the patterns of similarities and differences noted in the preceding section.

However, the Christian worldview provides more than a model for how genomes originated. Of equal import, this perspective informs a pressing present question: How shall we *use* our knowledge of genomes and our technical ability to manipulate them? For the Christian, ethical responses to these questions go beyond pure science and should be influenced by three factors: 1) the biblical account of creation, 2) current knowledge about genomics, and 3) humility in response to our incomplete and sometimes inaccurate understanding.

### *Engineering Genomes*

For Christians, the ultimate source of genomic information is the Creator God. This raises ethical questions about whether and how much that information should be manipulated. At what point does manipulation of information written by God Himself—the Logos of John 1:1—go beyond humans' authority? What constitutes appropriate genetic engineering?

Most people would agree that *some* ethical limit applies to genome manipulation. Christians may approach these issues from a perspective different from those with other worldviews, but even Christians debate the nature of our responsibility for God's creation (Genesis 1:26–28; Revelation 11:18). Does the "dominion" God gave humankind indicate that humans are free to do anything they fancy with the creation? Given that the Creator God of Christianity clothes the lilies in beauty and notes each sparrow that falls (Matthew 6:28–30; Luke 12:27–28; Matthew 10:29), it seems likely that He notices when we abuse His handiwork (this concept is developed in chapter 7).

One difficult area of genetic engineering for Christians is whether it is right to repair damaged genomes. Christians understand that the creation is damaged, so it seems reasonable that this damage would extend to genomes. Is it our job as Christians to edit and restore damaged genomes to their original state? How could we be certain of what that original state was? This issue becomes particularly acute when it comes to human genomes. Is there a line that should not be crossed between repairing damage and engineering "better" humans?

Does Adventist rejection of body-soul dualism mean that humans are only their living bodies? If the body is born "damaged," should we just accept that as God's will? Some have used this kind of logic to justify homosexual behavior among church members—God made homosexuals that way, so who are we to question it? However, would we embrace the same thinking if a way existed to repair mutations like the one that causes sickle cell anemia?

From my perspective, embracing concepts like an eternal soul, as espoused by most other Christians, only complicates the situation. Whatever answer one comes to about this issue, it should be firmly grounded in a biblical understanding of human nature, but even then the answers are not necessarily easy or evident; legitimate disagreements may exist among Christians. One thing that Christians should be able to agree on is that whatever our individual genetics, Jesus paid the ultimate price for all and we all look forward to the ultimate restoration God has promised to those who love Him.

### *Determining Ownership of Genomic Information*

Genomes store immense quantities of information, but who owns that information? Who should have access to it, and how can or should they use it? In our modern world, information is power; and information about you can benefit or harm you. For example, in the hands of your personal physician, information about whether you carry mutations of the *BRCA1* or *BRCA2* genes may save your life, since mutations in these tumor-suppressing genes place carriers at increased risk of breast cancer. Knowing that you are a carrier, you may screen more frequently for breast cancer, be more alert to changes in your body, and possibly even seek preemptive removal of breast tissue to eliminate the risk.

Despite these benefits, the knowledge that you carry a risk-enhancing mutation may also be problematic. What if no therapy is available? What if you wish to have children and yet fear passing on the mutation to them?

What if you want to marry but your potential spouse, on discovery of your genetic mutation, breaks the engagement—he or she doesn't want to marry someone who is "flawed"? The ethical quandaries and vulnerabilities seem endless. Determining what is ethical from a Christian perspective will involve serious soul searching.

## *Cloning*

Cloning represents another application of genomic knowledge with potential ethical implications. Clearly, a genome is not the same as an individual, and creating a new person or other organism with a genome identical to one already living will not create the same individual. Nature routinely produces clones via cuttings from plants, budding from yeast, and division of a fertilized egg in mammals (including humans) to form monozygotic twins. Study of these clones demonstrates that factors other than genetics have a major influence on the nature of organisms.

Given that producing clones does not represent copying individuals, what core ethical issues does "engineered" cloning raise? As Christians, we need to understand that systems of ethics are not ultimately driven by data but by worldviews and what they tell us about the nature of humans. A materialist who believes that humans simply represent a kind of animal produced by Darwinian evolution may be motivated by concerns different from those of a Christian. This is particularly true if materialists see cloning and associated technologies as a way to intelligently guide evolution via engineered eugenics.

As noted previously in this chapter (and to be discussed further in chapter 3), Seventh-day Adventist Christians reject body-soul dualism but see humans as whole beings—body, mind, and spirit. From this perspective, technologies associated with production of human clones may not be as troubling as they are for some other Christians who struggle with how eternal souls fit in with reproductive technologies in general. Still, at least for humans, practical issues with current technology render the prospect of human cloning deeply troubling because they run a high risk of producing profoundly damaged humans.

What might justify the inherent risks involved in human cloning? Is "just to show that we can" a good enough reason? What about therapeutic cloning? Does the possibility of curing an already living person justify cloning human embryos for the express purpose of harvesting or studying their cells?

These questions should deeply trouble all who believe in the basic value and dignity of human life, which explains the numerous papers devoted to these concerns—including from a Seventh-day Adventist perspective (Zuccarelli 2002, 2003).

In addition to questions about the *products* of human cloning, other ethical issues pertain to the *sources* of cloned genomes (and other needed biological materials). Who owns a person's cells? Is it ethical to clone someone's genome against his or her wishes? What if a person *does* want to make copies of him- or herself? Furthermore, because current cloning techniques rely on the use of eggs (into which the target genome is inserted), who (or what) will provide them? What reasonable inducements might be involved to procure donated eggs? Is it ethical to use eggs from other species? Back in 1998, scientists created embryos by inserting a human genome into a cow's egg (West 2003). Most people have a natural "yuck" reaction to this, but the investigators claimed that the procedure was perfectly ethical as long as the resulting embryos were destroyed within 14 days (BBC 1999). Imposition of an arbitrary time limit to ethical decisions about cross-species cloning may reflect the worldview of the investigators.

### *Asking, What Is a Human?*

Better understanding of human and other genomes has impacted not only how we view cells, but also the way we perceive ourselves and life around us. Before the genome was sequenced, Nobel Laureate Walter Gilbert claimed that knowing the human genome would tell us "What it is to be human" (quoted in Begley 2000). This statement represents more than simple hyperbole; the human genome does raise profound questions about what it is to be human.

Gilbert's conception of what it is to be human represents a curious application of reductionism, the philosophical position that complex systems are nothing more than the sum of their parts. In this view, a human being is nothing more than the sum of its constituent molecules; and, as those molecules all ultimately trace back to information encoded in human DNA, the genome actually does tell us what we are. Reductionism has profound implications for ethics, theology, medicine, and other branches of knowledge.

In contrast, Christians take a more holistic view of what constitutes a human. Yes, humans are made of atoms like the rest of the creation. In addition, however, each human is the special work of God's hands (Genesis

2:7), made in God's image (Genesis 1:26; 9:6), brought to life by God's breath (Genesis 2:7), and made "a little lower than the angels" (Psalm 8:5; Hebrews 2:7). Men and women are not an entity unto themselves but rather two parts of a single whole (Genesis 1:27) bound together as one flesh (Genesis 2:24; Matthew 19:5–6; Mark 10:8; 1 Corinthians 6:16; Ephesians 5:31) in the sacred institution of marriage—something true spiritually and biologically since both father and mother contribute complete genomes which are united together in their offspring. From a biblical perspective, humans are far more than atoms or information specifying how to arrange atoms; we are united to Christ in spirit, members of the larger body of Christ, and each of us the "temple of the Holy Ghost" (1 Corinthians 6:15–20).

If Christians reject reductionism, why should we be as excited as Gilbert about what genomes can tell us? Much of the hype about genomes involves serious exaggerations; the human genome may never tell us who we are or what it is to be human. Nonetheless, knowledge of our own genomes and those of other creatures does reveal many important attributes of living beings, highlighting the brilliance of the Creator, and giving insight into the history of life. As already stated, if nothing else, genomes should inspire wonder. One investigator elegantly expressed this wonder when the human genome was published: "What really astounds me is the architecture of life.... The system is extremely complex. It's like it was designed.... There's a huge intelligence there. I don't see that as being unscientific. Others may, but not me" (Mayers quoted in Abate 2001).

## Conclusions

Genomic data continues to accrue at an amazing pace, and our understanding of nature will continue to grow and change for the foreseeable future. Watching how people with different worldviews react and adapt to our changing understanding is sure to be interesting! And yet one important lesson is already clear: theories that seem certain today may crumble to dust tomorrow. My embarrassment when teaching molecular genetics, which I related earlier, gives one example of this lesson, but the principle applies to all teachers (and students) of science. In fact, I am virtually certain that some of what I've written in this chapter will prove to be wrong. This lesson may be especially helpful for Christians struggling with tension between the eternal truths of Scripture and current understandings of science.

As we mine genomes for information, I wonder what we will learn next. Up to this point, genomics has yielded a series of surprises that leaves me awestruck and humbled by my own ignorance of what remains to be discovered. Every person, every creature, every plant—indeed every living organism—is an exquisite repository of genetic information, and Christians have good reason to believe that we are "fearfully and wonderfully made" (Psalm 139:14).

Genomics reveals insights into the Creator's wisdom that those living before us could hardly have imagined. It also provides tools that we may use to benefit humanity and the rest of the creation. Ultimately, however, genomics sheds light on only one small if fascinating corner of the creation. Walter Gilbert was wrong when he said that knowing the human genome would tell us "What it is to be human" (quoted in Begley 2000). Rather, it is what we *do* with our knowledge of genomes that will reveal what we are.

## Literature Cited

Abate, T. 2001. Human genome map has scientists talking about the Divine: surprisingly low number of genes raises big questions. San Francisco Chronicle, February 19, B–1. http://www.sfgate.com/cgi-bin/article.cgi?file=/chronicle/archive/2001/02/19/BU141026.DTL.

Agarwal, S., and M. J. Behe. 1996. Non-conservative mutations are well tolerated in the globular region of Yeast Histone H4. Journal of Molecular Biology 255(3):401–411.

Ahituv, N., Y. Zhu, A. Visel, A. Holt, V. Afzal, L. A. Pennacchio, and E. M. Rubin. 2007. Deletion of ultraconserved elements yields viable mice. PLoS Biol 5(9):e234. doi:10.1371/journal.pbio.0050234.

BBC. 1999. Details of hybrid clone revealed. Web page published June 17, 1999, http://news.bbc.co.uk/hi/english/sci/tech/newsid_371000/371378.stm.

Begley, S. 2000. Decoding the human body. Newsweek, April 9, 2000. http://www.newsweek.com/id/83670.

Chan, Y. F. et al. 2010. Adaptive evolution of pelvic reduction in sticklebacks by recurrent deletion of a *Pitx1* enhancer. Science 327:302–305.

Clamp, M. et al. 2007. Distinguishing protein-coding and noncoding genes in the human genome. Proceedings of the National Academy of Sciences USA 104:19428–19433.

Denker, E., E. Bapteste, H. Le Guyader, M. Manuel, and N. Rabet. 2008. Horizontal gene transfer and the evolution of cnidarian stinging cells. Current Biology 18:R858–R859.

Dolgin, E. 2009. Human-chimp interbreeding challenged. Nature News, August 28, 2009, doi:10.1038/news.2009.870 News.

Gage, P. J., H. Suh, and S. A. Camper. 1999. The bicoid-related *Pitx* gene family in development. Mammalian Genome 10:197–200.

Haggerty, L. S., F. J. Martin, D. A. Fitzpatrick, and J. O. McInerney. 2009. Gene and genome trees conflict at many levels. Philosophical Transactions of the Royal Society B 364:2209–2219.

Hughes, J. F. et al. Page. 2010. Chimpanzee and human Y chromosomes are remarkably divergent in structure and gene content. Nature 463:536–539.

IJdo, J. W., A. Baldini, D. C. Ward, S. T. Reeders, and R. A. Wells. 1991. Origin of human chromosome 2: an ancestral telomere-telomere fusion. Proceedings of the National Academy of Sciences USA 88:9051–9055.

Khalturin, K., G. Hemmrich, S. Fraune, R. Augustin, and T. C. G. Bosch. 2009. More than just orphans: Are taxonomically-restricted genes important in evolution? Trends in Genetics 25:404–413.

Lamba, P., T. A. Hjalt, and D. J. Bernard. 2008. Novel forms of Paired-like homeodomain transcription factor 2 (*Pitx2*): Generation by alternative translation initiation and mRNA splicing. BMC Molecular Biology 9:31.

Lawton, G. 2009. Uprooting Darwin's tree. New Scientist 201(2692):34–39.

Lodish, H., D. Baltimore, A. Berk, S. L. Zipursky, P. Matsudaira, and J. Darnell. 1995. Molecular cell biology, 3rd ed. Scientific American Books, New York.

Makalowski, W. 2003. Not junk after all. Science 300:5623.

Margulis, L., and D. Sagan. 2002. Acquiring genomes: A theory of the origins of species. Basic Books, New York.

Ohno, S. 1972. So much "junk" DNA in our genome. Brookhaven symposia in biology. Pp. 366–70 in Evolution of genetic systems (H. H. Smith, ed.). Gordon and Breach, New York.

Pagán Westphal, S. 2004. Life goes on without "vital" DNA. New Scientist 182 (2450):18. http://www.newscientist.com/article/dn5063-life-goes-on-without-vital-dna.html.

Pandolfi, P. 2010. quoted in: Science Daily. June 24, 2010. http://www.sciencedaily.com/releases/2010/06/100623132102.htm.

Patterson, N., D. J. Richter, S. Gnerre, E. S. Lander, and D. Reich. 2006. Genetic evidence for complex speciation of humans and chimpanzees. Nature 441:1103–1108.

Pheasant, M., and J. S. Mattick. 2007. Raising the estimate of functional human sequences. Genome Research 17:1245–1253.

Poliseno, L., L. Salmena, J. Zhang, B. Brett Carver, W. J. Haveman, and P. P. Pandolfi. 2010. A coding-independent function of gene and pseudogene mRNAs regulates tumour biology. Nature 465:1033–1038.

Ponting, C., and A. P. Jackson. 2005. Evolution of primary microcephaly genes and the enlargement of primate brains. Current Opinion in Genetics & Development 15:241–248.

RIKEN Genome Exploration Research Group and Genome Science Group (Genome Network Project Core Group) and the FANTOM Consortium. 2005. Antisense transcription in the mammalian transcriptome. Science 309:1564–1566.

Robinson, D. E. 1931. Amalgamation versus evolution. Elmshaven, St. Helena, California. White Document File 316, Heritage Room, Loma Linda University.

Sapp, J. 1994. Evolution by association: A history of symbiosis. Oxford University Press, New York.

Smith, U. 1866. "The visions—objections answered: Obj. 37," Advent Review and Sabbath Herald, July 31, 1866, 65–66.

Standish, T. 2002. Rushing to judgment: Functionality in noncoding or "junk" DNA. Origins 53:7–30.

Tam, O. H. et al. 2008. Pseudogene-derived small interfering RNAs regulate gene expression in mouse oocytes. Nature 453:534–538.

Theobald, D. L. 2010. A formal test of the theory of universal common ancestry. Nature 465:219–222.

West, M. D. 2003. Human therapeutic cloning: A maelstrom of controversy. Chapter 7 in The Immortal Cell: One scientist's quest to solve the mystery of human ageing. Doubleday, New York.

Williamson, D. I. 1992. Larvae and evolution: Toward a new zoology. Chapman and Hall, New York.

Williamson, D. I. 2001. Larval transfer and the origin of larvae. Zoological Journal of the Linnean Society 131:111–122.

Woese, C. R. 2002. On the evolution of cells. Proceedings of the National Academy of Sciences USA 99:8742–8747.

Wood, T. C. 2008. Horse fossils and the nature of science. Answers Magazine 3(4):74–77.
Yunis, J. J., and O. Prakash. 1982. The origin of man: A chromosomal pictorial legacy. Science 215:1525–1530.
Yunis, J. J., J. R. Sawyer, and K. Dunham. 1980. The striking resemblance of high-resolution G-banded chromosomes of man and chimpanzee. Science 208:1145–1148.
Zhang, C., W. H. Li, A. R. Krainer, and M. Q. Zhang. 2008. RNA landscape of evolution for optimal exon and intron discrimination. Proceedings of the National Academy of Sciences USA 105:5797–5802.
Zuccarelli, A. 2002. Ethical choices in the genetic age. Part 1: Reproductive cloning. Journal of Adventist Education 64(5):37–42.
Zuccarelli, A. 2003. Ethical choices in the genetic age. Part 2: Embryonic science. Journal of Adventist Education 65(3):40–47.

Chapter Three

# BEING HUMANS: BIOLOGY, FAITH, AND HUMAN NATURE

**Karl G. D. Bailey**

"You," wrote Francis Crick in the opening lines of *The Astonishing Hypothesis,* "your joys and your sorrows, your memories and your ambitions, your sense of personal identity and free will, are in fact no more than the behavior of a vast assembly of nerve cells" (1994:3). In the decade and a half since Crick made this claim, the growth and popularization of brain-imaging research has led to a growing perception among scientists and the general public that we are, indeed, nothing more than our biology—that human nature both reduces to and is determined by biological structures and processes. What does this mean for Adventist Christians, who believe that free will is real and that our choices have eternal implications? What then of evil and sin, of mercy and justice, of grace and salvation? Of course, questions of God, good, evil, human actions, and free will are not new—religious leaders in Jesus's time debated some of the same issues (Klawans 2009)—but current discussions of human nature must account for our biological nature.

In this chapter, I describe an integration of neuroscience and cognitive science research from a Seventh-day Adventist perspective on human nature. I will begin with some basic principles of the nervous system, the mind, and social interaction framed by an Adventist perspective. I will then examine consciousness and free will, noting points of contact among philosophy, neuroscientific research, and Adventist thought. Finally, I will discuss how our understanding of human nature may impact the kinds of people we become, arguing that careful thinking about consciousness and free will should play a significant role in how we live out our faith in our daily lives. One of my main concerns in writing this chapter is that if we, as Christians, fail to examine the issues raised by advances in neuroscience, we may accept nonbiblical positions by default; already ideas extrapolated from neuroscience are impacting Western society through education (Goswami 2006) and the court system (Morse 2008).

## Biology, Brain, and Mind

### *The Biology of the Brain*

The basic biological components of the human nervous system are cells (neurons and glial cells) and the connections between those cells (synapses). I will focus on neurons in this chapter, but glial cells are also believed to play an intricate role in coordinating neural activity (Fields 2004). Neurons conduct information from place to place as electrical impulses by means of ions moving into and out of the cells. At the places where neurons meet each other—synapses—packets of chemicals (*neurotransmitters*) are released and then diffuse across a very small gap (the *synaptic cleft*) and attach to proteins (*receptors*) on the other side, leading more ions to move into and out of the next neuron. (Imagine a fistful of keys diffusing across a hallway—the synapse—sliding into locks, and opening doors on the other side.) Depending on which receptor is activated, the receiving neuron may become more or less likely to fire. If the sum of all of this activity (the more-or-less likelihoods) at any given time reaches a certain threshold in the receiving neuron, it will fire, passing on information to yet other cells. Each neuron thus sends information to and receives information from many other neurons. This sending and receiving, coordinating and firing, happens over and over, moment by moment on a grand scale: millions of your neurons are firing at any given time, millions are not, and some neuroscientists claim that the resulting pattern fully determines *you* (Crick 1994).

Longer-term changes also occur when neurotransmitters attach to receptors: a cascade of chemical signals leads to the expression of genes from the DNA library in the nucleus, producing proteins that change the structure and function of the neuron. In some cases, the neuron becomes more sensitive to certain input, while in others it becomes less sensitive; it may grow new connections or lose old connections; it may enlarge or shrink (Lamprecht and LeDoux 2004). These are changes to the very structure of the brain that make neural circuits either more or less likely to fire in the future. Thus, not only is your brain actively involved as you read this chapter, the very act is—quite literally—also changing the physical structure of your brain (Beauregard 2007)!

These changes to physical structure encode what information goes with what: neurons are coincidence detectors par excellence (Crick and

Koch 2003). This means that you learn, not by storing logical rules like a computer, but by slowly shaping an understanding of what information goes with what and changing the way you process the world as a result. Over time, that understanding becomes an expectation that certain things will go together in certain circumstances. This sensitivity to coincidence and the subsequent development of expectation at the most basic processing level of the brain probably underlie the human tendency to see cause and effect everywhere and to see what you expect to see, even when reality contradicts your view of yourself (Dunning 2005).

Two possible implications emerge from this short description of how the brain works (see chapter 3 of Aamodt and Wang [2008] for a slightly longer, but more thorough account). First, all brain activity requires energy in the form of (mainly) glucose (Gailliot et al. 2007). Even small changes in levels of glucose can affect brain function,[1] because the brain is able to consume glucose faster than it can be replenished. In fact, the more efficiently glucose is made available to and used by the brain, the better people perform on mental tasks (Donohoe and Benton 1999).

A second possible implication of the preceding description of the human brain, which we discussed at the beginning of this chapter, is that it suggests principles at the level of neurons and synapses that might describe how learning and behavior work—without recourse to consciousness, free will, or thinking as real causes. However, the nothing-but-neurons claim is *not* directly implied by the structure of the nervous system; all that is implied is that certain principles govern how neurons function *at the level of neurons.*

---

1. This insatiable demand for glucose underlies two modern techniques of brain imaging: functional magnetic resonance imaging (fMRI) and positron emission tomography (PET). These techniques generate images of the brain based on changes in blood flow needed to bring more glucose to active neurons. Brain imaging has proved to be a useful tool for testing hypotheses about how the mind works, although it only documents correlations between brain activity and mental state. Curiously, the technique has revealed biases in human cognition that give insight into how we think about our own nature. For example, nonspecialists treat brain images as more convincing and direct measures of the mind than they actually are; laypersons are more likely to accept illogical and circular arguments when shown an fMRI scan—or even when they hear mention of brain function (McCabe and Castel 2008; Weisberg et al. 2008)! This bias may indicate that human beings are, by nature, "intuitive dualists" (Bloom 2004; Weisberg 2008), believing that they are composed of two separate parts: material bodies and immaterial souls.

The denial of consciousness and willpower as real causes that affect the function of neurons requires us to *assume* that neural principles will be sufficient to explain all of human learning and behavior, including conscious experience. However, neuroscience has not demonstrated this claim, and there are good reasons to think that it never will (Murphy 2009). For example, details of the complexity of human language are not predicted or explained by the details of neuronal function, nor is the existence of language itself. Descriptions at higher levels of analysis (those of cognitive psychology and linguistics) are necessary to fully account for what human language is and how it works. Neuroscience certainly *informs* this study—by providing useful limitations on possible models for the nature and function of language—but it does not directly answer questions that arise at other levels of description and explanation (Murphy 2009). Precisely how these levels relate to each other, however, is a matter of debate, framed to a great extent by differences in philosophy. How do various philosophies answer the big questions about biology and human nature that are the focus of this chapter?

### *Terms and Teams*

Scholars have developed different interpretations of the relationship between the biology of the brain and human nature. To communicate clearly about these interpretations, we need a set of philosophical terms to help us identify the major players in the ongoing discussion of what humans are. To use an analogy from the world of sports, these terms act much like the color of fans' clothing or players' jerseys at a sporting event: they identify team loyalty at a glance and help to classify complex and detailed ideas. Moreover, the concept of team loyalty is useful in understanding the tenor of the discussion in this area, as questions of human nature are often argued with a passion fit for a stadium or arena, because they directly impact how we view our place in the universe! We can organize these terms (teams!) by the different answers they give to key questions about human nature (Fig. 1).

*Are minds and bodies separate or unified (Fig. 1A)?* Do you have a separate soul or mind that can exist as you, apart from your body? Members of *Team Monism* believe that humans are indivisible, unified entities and that neither mind, body, nor soul can be extracted from a person—and still have a person remain. In contrast, *Team Dualism* claims that humans are made up of separate material and immaterial (spiritual or mental) components that exist in different realities—the reality of matter and that of mind—but which can still interact (Popper and Eccles 1983). Most human beings are probably dualists, at least instinctively (Weisberg 2008; Bloom 2004). However, most neuroscientists are monists, as are Adventists (consider, for example, the Adventist doctrine of the state of the dead). The monist view leads to a second question.

*What is the basic "stuff" that human beings are made from?* Most monists are also on *Team Materialism*—they believe that human beings are made of matter—but a few monists suggest that only thought or spirit is real (this is a small cheering section for *Team Idealism*). Here, again, there is general consensus between most neuroscientists and Adventists that humans are formed of matter. However, materialists disagree about how to answer a third question.

*Can we explain all of human nature using the principles that describe the basic building blocks of human beings (Fig. 1B)?* The nothing-but-neurons view, held by members of *Team Reductionism,* attempts to explain all human nature by reducing it to the basic principles of function at the level of neurons and synapses.[2] However, not all monists or materialists are reductionists; some *nonreductive* monists, members of *Team Holism,* claim that at each additional level of human cognition, there are processes that cannot be fully reduced to and derived from the

---

2. Strictly speaking, this is a strong form of ontological and theoretical reductionism that Nancey Murphy (2009) refers to as causal reductionism, or the belief that everything that happens is predetermined, from the bottom up, by the principles and properties that govern the basic building blocks of the universe. Ontology refers to the science of being—questions about where our nature comes from—and so strong ontological reductionism argues that our nature is based on the principles of the most basic forms of matter (if you are a materialist, at least). Theoretical reductionism is the idea that the theories at any level of the sciences can be reduced to the theories of levels below, and ultimately to a supertheory based in physics. In practice, there are few cases where this has been possible (Murphy 2009). Other forms of reductionism exist. Methodological reductionism is the very successful approach in science that involves breaking down the world into parts and studying the function and behavior of those parts separately in order to properly understand the world. Even scientists who do not subscribe to Crick's ontological reductionism likely participate in methodological reductionism—it is what makes the scientific endeavor tractable. Weaker forms of ontological reductionism exist as well that simply stipulate that nothing new (like an immaterial soul) is added at any level (Murphy 2009).

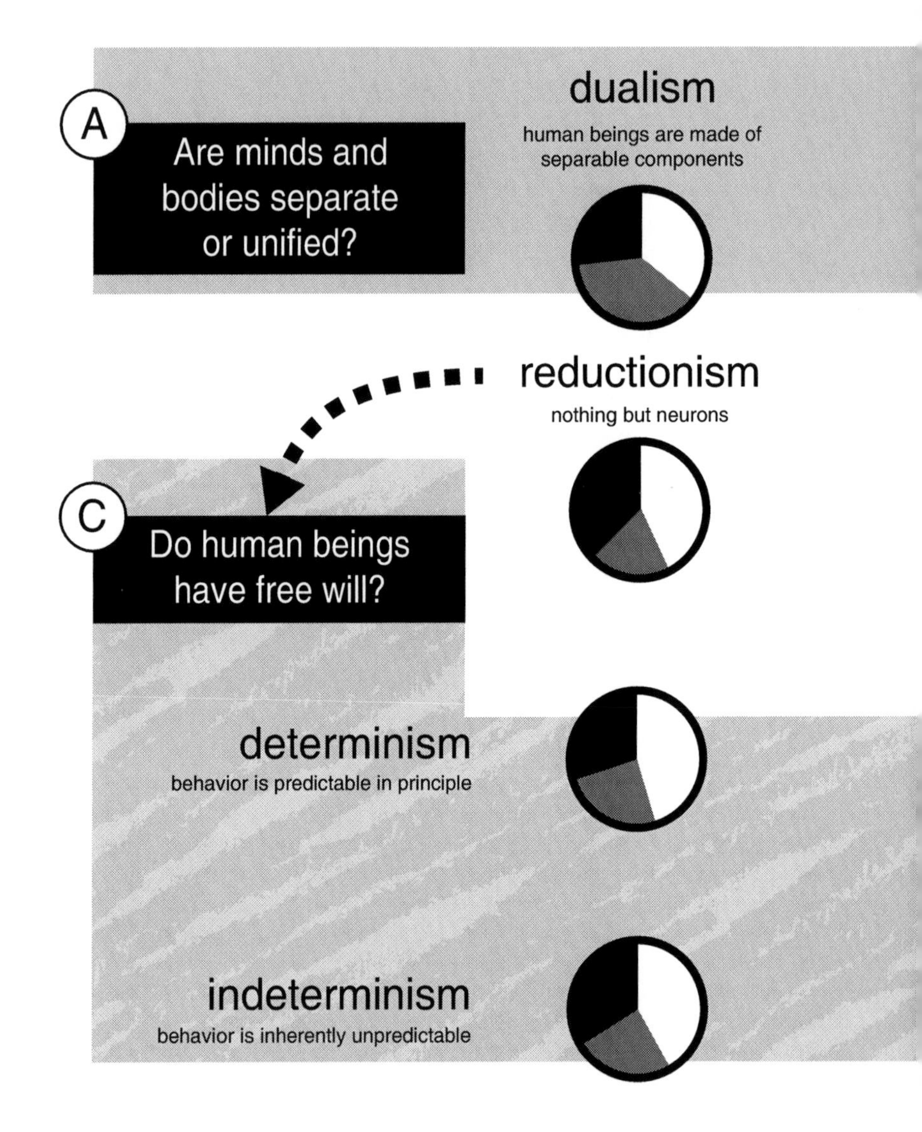


**Figure 1**—Philosophical perspectives on human nature and free will as they relate to 3 questions: A) whether minds and bodies are separate or unified, B) whether human nature is fully explained by material building blocks, and C) whether—and to what degree—humans

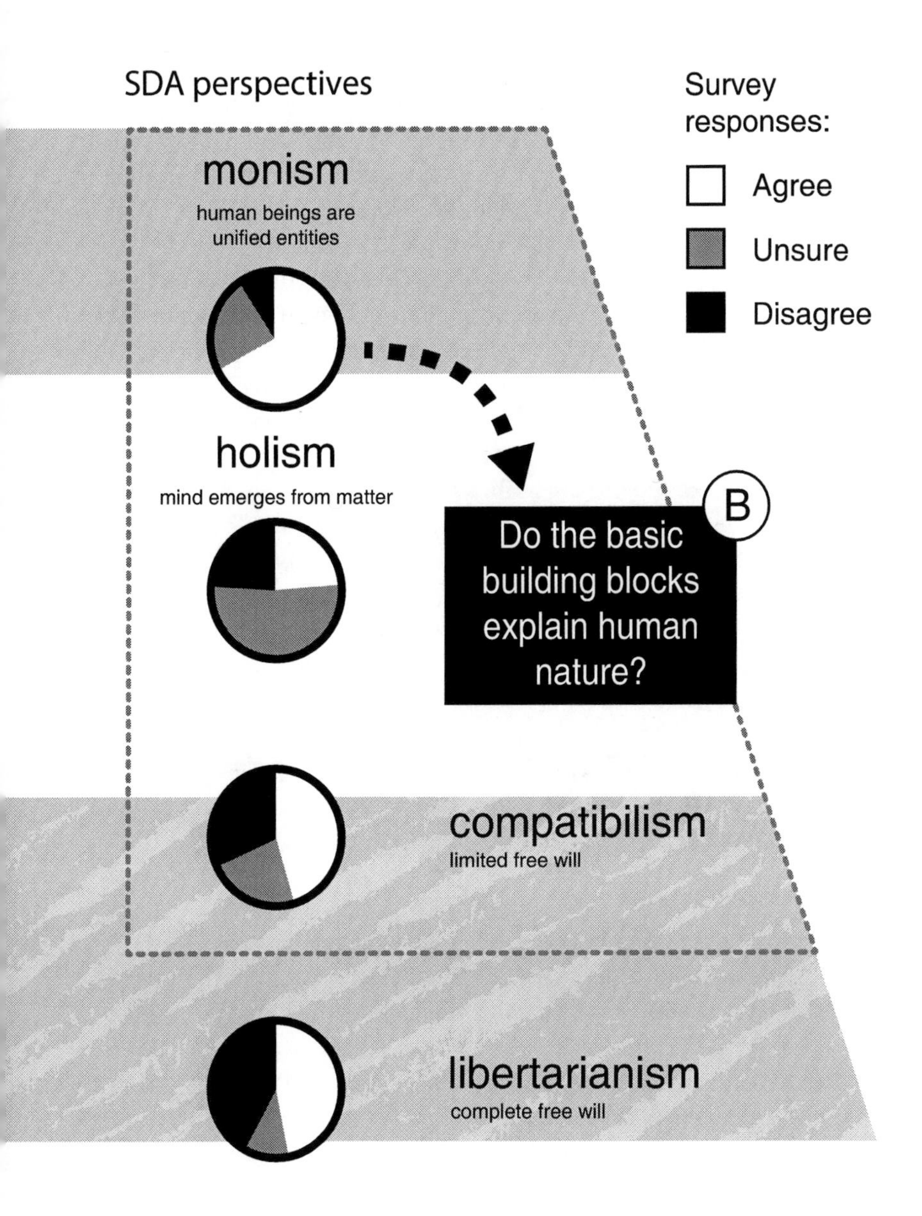


have free will. The perspectives consistent with Adventist teaching are enclosed in the dotted polygon. Also, the proportions of 828 Adventist college students who agree, disagree, or express uncertainty about each perspective are given (based on data collected by the author).

simpler principles of underlying levels (i.e., you cannot explain the mind based solely on the principles of neural function). On this point, Adventists, who offer a holistic view of human nature, part company with some neuroscientists, who are firm reductionists, but are in agreement with others, who affirm holism. Reductionists and holists likewise differ in how they answer a final question.

*Do humans have free will (Fig. 1C)?* Most reductionists are members of *Team Determinism;* they claim that future states of the brain are completely predictable (at least in principle) given complete knowledge of the state of the brain now, thus they have no room for free will in their explanation of human cognition and behavior. Members of *Team Indeterminism* attempt to preserve free will by appealing to unpredictable (e.g., quantum) events in the structure of matter, thus rendering the future as unknowable (Hameroff and Penrose 2003; see Koch and Hepp 2006 for a critique of this interpretation of consciousness and free will). These two views contrast with those held by members of *Team Libertarianism,* who believe humans have complete free will (when faced with any choice, you could have chosen otherwise), and those who support *Team Compatibilism.* The latter position holds that both natural, material processes *and* free will may cause human behavior (Gomes 2007) within the world of matter (free will is the freedom to act as you choose, not the requirement that choices be unconstrained or undetermined). As we shall see, Adventists hold a compatibilist view of human nature, at least in theory.

## *Making Up the Mind*

There is a big jump between our understanding of brain physiology and the function of the human mind. We still do not know how to translate what the brain is doing into what the mind is doing, or to summarize what is happening in simple principles (Bechtel 1994)—despite thousands of studies that have used brain imaging to study the mind as well as recent advances in statistical modeling (Poldrack et al. 2009). Nevertheless, most cognitive psychologists[3] agree on a general description of the structure of

3. Cognitive psychology is a branch of experimental psychology, a basic research discipline that uses careful observation and experimentation to uncover the principles and mechanisms underlying human and animal learning and behavior. In this endeavor, experimental psychology overlaps with the traditional biological discipline of ethology (the study of animal behavior). However, since the Cognitive Revolution of the 1950s and 1960s, experimental psychology has moved in the direction of considering the nature

the mind (e.g., Pinker 1999; Peterson 2003). In this view, the mind does three different kinds of things: (1) sensation and perception; (2) learning and remembering; and (3) processing, predicting, and responding. These processes may respond to events in the world, or they may be generated internally during simulations of the past or future.

The most important principle derived from the study of the mind is that human minds are limited. *Limited* is used here in two senses: limits on conscious experience and access, and limits on processing. First, our conscious experience (what we often think of when we refer to the *mind*) does not contain everything that may be observed in the world or recalled from memory; we often fail to see a stop sign until the last moment, neglect to hear someone ask us to take out the trash, or are stumped when we try to recall the name of a classmate we have not seen in years. Moreover, the moments when we are aware of our limitations are few and far between; most of the time we are blissfully unaware of what we are missing or do not know (Dunning 2005).

The principle of limitation includes more than our limited ability to take in and recall information; it also reflects limits to how much of our mental function we consciously experience and have access to. Consider the following example. People with damage to the visual cortex of the brain sometimes develop a syndrome called blindsight. Such individuals can accurately point to the location of a spot of light even though they are blind and lack conscious awareness of the light (Weiskrantz et al. 1974; Barbur et al. 1980; Goodale et al. 1991; Cowey 2004)—a form of sight without conscious access and experience. The blindsight example suggests that our brains process more information than we are aware of at any given time. Indeed, much of the constant, daily rewiring of the brain results from the unconscious processing of information. As a result, even in the undamaged areas, the brains of people with blindsight are eventually wired differently than the brains of sighted people (Bridge et al. 2008), and this unconscious rewiring may lead to changes in conscious

of and building models of internal mental states. Thus, most experimental psychologists now use a variety of measurements of human behavior to test hypotheses about the internal mental processes that underlie learning and behavior. Since experimental psychology was founded as a discipline by scientists trained in physiology and medicine, it probably should be considered a biological science (Wilson 1975/2000; Goodwin 1999; Ward 2006).

experience. In sum, the conscious mind involves a small part of the brain's function; most of what goes on in the brain remains inaccessible to the conscious mind, but changes the conscious mind nonetheless.

The second sense in which the human mind is limited is that our minds cannot process all of the information that we *are* aware of. We have limits in what we can pay attention to, how much we can hold in memory at any given time, and in our ability to solve difficult and complex problems. These limits leave us standing in a room, having forgotten why we are there! This limitation especially applies when we are under pressure (Baddeley 2001; Beilock and Carr 2005).

### *Exploring the Question of Human Nature: An Adventist Answer*

So far, I have described the brain and mind as self-modifying entities that are limited by glucose availability and information processing. As noted previously, most neuroscientists assume, at least implicitly, a monist view of human nature which holds that the mind and the body are inseparable. Otherwise, why study the mind by recording blood flow and electrical activity in the brain? Some scientists also argue for reductionism, and for a deterministic view of human nature. However, other scientists point to differences in phenomena at different levels of analysis—from neurons to brain areas to mind to social interaction—which challenge strong reductionism. This holistic view has been termed *nonreductive physicalism* (Brown et al. 1998), and it is consistent with a Seventh-day Adventist view of human nature (Fig. 1B). Indeed, the Adventist doctrinal statement on human nature[4] identifies humans as "an indivisible unity of mind, body, and spirit." We can further describe an Adventist view of human nature as having the following three components:

---

4. The Seventh-day Adventist fundamental belief on human nature reads as follows: "Man and woman were made in the image of God with individuality, the power and freedom to think and to do. Though created free beings, each is an indivisible unity of body, mind, and spirit, dependent upon God for life and breath and all else. When our first parents disobeyed God, they denied their dependence upon Him and fell from their high position under God. The image of God in them was marred and they became subject to death. Their descendants [sic] share this fallen nature and its consequences. They are born with weaknesses and tendencies to evil. But God in Christ reconciled the world to Himself and by His Spirit restores in penitent mortals the image of their Maker. Created for the glory of God, they are called to love Him and one another, and to care for their environment. (Gen. 1:26–28; 2:7; Ps. 8:4–8; Acts 17:24–28; Gen. 3; Ps. 51:5; Rom. 5:12–17; 2 Cor. 5:19, 20; Ps. 51:10; 1 John 4:7, 8, 11, 20; Gen. 2:15.)"

1. Adventists believe that human beings are indivisible selves (Fig. 1A) and that factors that affect any aspect of a person will affect all other aspects of that person (Kuntaraf and Liwidjaja-Kuntaraf 2008). It is thus valid and indeed necessary to study all of these aspects of the person; they are not reducible to each other or interchangeable but rather represent different aspects of personhood.
2. Adventists believe that human beings have free will and that they can and do make intentional choices that are not predetermined by neural structures or environmental factors. However, Adventists also believe that human free will is limited because of sin and our material nature; some choices are not always available for reasons of ability, character, experience, or environment. Most importantly, we can deny or facilitate certain *future* choices based on our *present* choices. Thus, free will is limited, and human beings remain dependent on God. This is a form of compatibilism (Fig. 1C).
3. Adventists believe that human beings exist in relationship to particular social and physical environments, and that God's provision of free will demands a responsibility toward the created world and social world around us. Thus, Adventists see free will as a commission to do as we ought—not as a license to do as we please.

Not all Christians embrace all aspects of the Adventist view of human nature. Over the history of Christianity, debates have raged about whether God has ordained all things, or merely knows what will or may occur; whether God has sovereign control over all of the universe, or is self-limited by granting freedom to human beings; whether salvation is predestined or freely chosen; and whether the human self is made up of one (holistic), two (body and soul), or three (body, soul, and spirit) parts (Basinger and Basinger 1986; Brown et al. 1998; Picirilli 2002; Tonstad 2008; Boyd and Eddy 2009). These different views are not just academic in nature; they shape how religions, churches, and individuals make decisions and pursue priorities (Tonstad 2008).

A recent unpublished study from our laboratory suggests that many Adventist college students are affected both by Adventist teachings about human nature as well as by the ideas in the prevailing culture (pie charts in Fig. 1). For example, the majority of respondents held a monist (versus dualist) view of human nature (Fig. 1A), consistent with Adventist thought, but nearly half reported reductionist beliefs (Fig. 1B). When asked about their views on free will, many reflected uncertainty and confusion: about 40–45% of respondents agreed with all 4 positions on free will, indicating that some students simultaneously held conflicting beliefs (Fig. 1C). These results indicate that both sacred and secular ideas about human nature have influenced our understanding, whether we think about them intentionally or not.

*Recognizing a Need for Integration*

Let us summarize. Neuroscientists and cognitive scientists have discovered a great deal about the brain and mind, not the least of which is that we still have much to learn! However, what we know about brain function—at the level of neurons—suggests that the brain learns the relationships between events and information by making small structural changes over time, and that the processing needed to identify those relationships is limited by glucose availability. Limitations also apply at the level of the mind; our conscious experience provides an incomplete picture of our mental processing, and we are able to process only limited amounts of information at any given time. Although a reductionist view offers one interpretation of these discoveries, other views are possible as well—including nonreductive physicalism or holism, consistent with an Adventist view of human nature.

However, our study of how Adventist students view free will suggests that many have not adequately integrated Adventist teaching with scientific and cultural ideas and beliefs about human nature; thus, Adventist students likely are developing their understanding of human nature without much intentional thought. While this might seem trivial, beliefs about human nature directly shape what people do and how much effort they put into their activities (Dweck 2006)—that is, how people live their lives. Moreover, many popular accounts of human nature go far beyond—or even ignore—the scientific data to make strong but unsupported claims that often are repeated as truth, even when those claims contradict the scientific evidence and the speaker's worldview (Lilienfeld et al. 2010). Thus, it is important for Adventists to intentionally examine the biblical doctrine of human nature and related scientific evidence, to seek integration where possible, and to note areas where distinctive differences exist.

## Taking a Closer Look at Consciousness and Free Will

In the following sections, we will examine two major aspects of human nature: consciousness and free will. Consciousness is an important precursor to free will because it allows for the possibility of controlled (as opposed to automatic) actions, for re-experiencing past decisions, for imagining future decisions, and for intentional planning. Free will adds a volitional aspect to consciousness: we control our actions, and do not merely experience them. When we integrate these concepts with the scientific principles described earlier in this chapter, as well as with an Adventist worldview, it is possible, I believe, to derive a strong argument for an intentional Christian walk.

### *Contemplating Consciousness*

Consciousness, which is subjective and private, is difficult to define (Velmans 2009). However, most scientific discussions of consciousness begin with the basic idea that the awareness of an experience by you yourself could be considered consciousness (Nagel 1974; Edelman and Tononi 2001), in which case the goal of the study of consciousness is to explain subjective experience. Cognitive scientists encounter a number of issues when they attempt to explain subjective experiences: demonstrating that consciousness is real, understanding the biological basis for consciousness, and determining whether consciousness helps explain human behavior.

We will now turn to the first issue and consider the evidence for the reality of conscious experience. Demonstrating that conscious experience is real—that is, that *other* people are actually having the experiences that they describe—is surprisingly difficult. Philosophers have long noted that the quality and content of your conscious experience (what cognitive scientists term *qualia;* Ramachandran and Blakeslee 1998; Ramachandran 2004) might be different from mine. For you, *red* or *middle C* or *the number 3* might be experiences that are very different from mine. Do we have evidence that this claim corresponds to reality? Yes, at least for certain people. For example, individuals with a syndrome known as synesthesia may experience one kind of sensory input with another sense—for example, particular letters and numbers may be experienced as particular colors, or specific tastes as shapes! These people report different qualia than people without synesthesia, and their reports have been confirmed experimentally

(Ramachandran and Blakeslee 1998; Ramachandran 2004; Hubbard and Ramachandran 2005; Kadosh et al. 2009).

The development of noninvasive brain-imaging techniques has played a major role in demonstrating the reality of conscious experience because imaging makes it possible to record brain states that occur during known conscious processes. Let us consider one example. Serious ethical questions arise when families must decide how to deal with individuals classified as being in persistent vegetative states who, by definition, should not have conscious experiences (the Terri Schiavo case is one such example; Cranford 2005). Recent studies suggest that a small number of these patients may actually be minimally conscious: they show increases in brain activity within visual and motor areas when asked to imagine performing a task, even though they show no overt responses (Owen et al. 2006; Monti et al. 2010). These data raise significant questions about how to assess and treat patients in persistent vegetative states, and support the distinction between observable behavior and conscious experience—the former may be lost without losing the latter.

Given that subjective conscious experience is real, how does it emerge from the biology of the brain? The dominant and best current model suggests that loops of two-way connections between brain regions, termed *re-entrant connections,* pass information back and forth between these regions, allowing this information to be refined and enhanced (like feedback building between a microphone and a speaker) to the point of consciousness (Edelman and Tononi 2001). This model predicts that consciousness develops, at minimum, over multiple loops of neural activity (Dehaene and Naccache 2001; Crick and Koch 2003; Greenfield and Collins 2005; Tononi and Koch 2008; see McGovern and Baars 2007 and Kouider 2009 for reviews) and thus faces a fundamental speed limit: the firing and transmission rates of neurons in the brain—about 20 miles per hour for most myelinated neurons that connect the two hemispheres of the brain (Wang et al. 2008; Ringo et al. 1994). Consistent with this prediction, the experimental study of vision demonstrates that conscious awareness of a visual event lags behind the actual event by at least 80 milliseconds and up to 150–250 milliseconds (Eagleman and Sejnowski 2000; Rabbitt 2002; Koch 2004).

The relatively slow emergence of consciousness suggests a third issue. If our conscious experience is consistently tens to hundreds of milliseconds in the past, what does consciousness *do* for us? Consider the following hypotheses. Consciousness might create a unified experience (Lombardi et al. 1987) and help people recall, compare, and contrast their experiences with memory (Tononi 2004); it may summarize what is happening right now (Koch 2004); or it might be necessary for creative and novel behavior, stable long-term memory, and the development of spontaneous intentions to act voluntarily (Dehaene and Naccache 2001). In other words, consciousness helps us figure out who we are and what we are doing so that we can intentionally change ourselves and our world—both at the level of our brains and ourselves (Posner and Rothbart 1998)—but over time scales of much greater duration than the few 100 milliseconds characteristic of our immediate perceptions and responses to the world.

Furthermore, consciousness allows for immersive mental time travel—the ability to consciously experience our memory of the past, and to imagine the future—which frees humans from reacting solely to the circumstances and demands of the here-and-now (Wheeler et al. 1997; Suddendorf and Busby 2005). Indeed, the network of brain regions that underlies conscious autobiographical recollection of the past seems to be highly involved in conscious "pre-experiencing" of the future (Botzung et al. 2008). This allows people to act not only on future goals, but also to put aside current motivations in order to prepare for and bring about future possibilities. This view of consciousness—as the cognitive function that allows us to integrate our past, present, and future—is directly applicable to an Adventist worldview that derives meaning from time (the Sabbath, prophecy, and history) as well as hope for the future (the Second Advent).

Although consciousness does important work for us, conscious experience sometimes does not match the real world. Consider the following examples. Following a stroke in the right hemisphere, some patients who are paralyzed on the left side of the body develop a syndrome known as denial: they invent a story to explain why they are in fact *not* paralyzed (Ramachandran and Blakeslee 1998). In these cases, the stroke apparently disrupts regions of the brain that identify discrepancies between current understanding and the real world, thus the undamaged left hemisphere is free to maintain an increasingly delusional prestroke understanding of the world. Significantly, similar discrepancies between current understanding and reality may occur in healthy brains, leading to the development of false memories (Schacter 2001; Principe et al. 2006; Wade et al. 2002).

To summarize, then, consciousness appears to be real and to serve important functions in human experience, but it may also incorrectly reflect the state of the world. This represents a human limitation often discussed by biblical authors (e.g., the book of Isaiah or chapters 7 and 8 of Romans), who seek to draw humans back to dependence on God. When we separate from God and turn a blind eye to our God-given limitations, our conscious perception of the world becomes distorted, and what would formerly produce revulsion may become a source of pleasure and desire (Isaiah 5:20). Prophets and psychologists alike have catalogued the ease with which this occurs (Miller 2004; Zimbardo 2008). At the same time, an understanding of human limitations may lead us to seek justice, mercy, and humility given our common heritage of frailty. In addition, a holistic view of human beings leads us to seek restoration for the whole person—for both ourselves and for others—and not work solely for the salvation of body, mind, or soul (Kuntaraf and Liwidjaja-Kuntaraf 2008). This approach to human nature, which is nonreductive but materialist and monist, motivates the Adventist understanding of gospel work as service to the whole person, both in our individual choices and in evangelism. And, because conscious and nonconscious processes give rise to each other, a holistic view suggests that everything matters: character development (i.e., the development of the conscious and nonconscious aspects of mind, body, and spirit) is the work of a lifetime, and consciousness may be the key to acting in the here-and-now with an awareness of the past and hope for the future.

### *Finding Free Will*

Of course, by suggesting that human beings can develop their character, I am implicitly suggesting that human beings have causal control over themselves: that is, humans have free will. Free will requires two elements: the presence of multiple, viable options from which to choose, and the absence of coercion (Tonstad 2008). The deterministic, nothing-but-neurons view denies the presence of free choice; it expects that the structure of the nervous system in interaction with the environment will always lead to a predetermined outcome for a given human being in a given situation. In this view, both the experience of consciousness and the intention to act are illusions that have no real impact on the world. In contrast, the nonreductive holism of Adventist thought suggests that both consciousness and free will affect the world; they are necessary for both rebellion and repentance. This view also suggests that while choice is possible, not all choices are always available because of circumstances both within and outside our control (Picirilli 2002). Again, we are limited.

How does this perspective—that free will is real but limited—intersect with what is known about what happens in the brain when we make choices? One set of studies (e.g., Libet et al. 1983; Libet 1999) took advantage of an observation from the 1960s: when human beings make an intentional, voluntary movement (such as intentionally lifting a finger), there is a negative electrical potential, termed the *readiness potential,* that is generated by large populations of neurons about a second prior to the occurrence of the movement (Kornhuber and Deecke 1965). Initially, investigators assumed that the voluntary intention was generated first, followed by the readiness potential, and then the action itself. However, Libet and his colleagues (1983) obtained shocking results in a careful experimental test: the readiness potential occurred *first* by half a second, followed by the estimate of intention to act, and then the action. They interpreted this to mean that conscious intentions did not initiate the movement. However, Libet wanted to rescue conscious free will, so he suggested that free will lies in the ability to cancel a movement (an idea jokingly referred to as "free won't") in the time remaining between the readiness potential and the action (Libet et al. 1983; Libet 1999). Another study found that the outcome of a two-option choice can be predicted (although not perfectly) up to ten seconds before subjects reported a conscious decision to move, and that the timing of the choice may be predicted up to five seconds before the decision. Correlated changes in brain activity occur long before subjects report any conscious intention (Soon et al. 2008).

What do these results suggest about free will? To begin with, available data only show a consistent correlation: the readiness potential consistently occurs prior to movement. They do not prove that the potential *causes* intention or vice versa (Gomes 1999, 2007). Moreover, other studies have found that the readiness potential is generated even in cases where people are told to plan a movement and then cancel it at the last minute; they are told to do both things ahead of time (Gomes 2007). Thus, the readiness potential does not indicate that an action *must* occur but that it *may* occur (Gomes 1999). Furthermore, these experiments ask subjects to be aware of their conscious processes, a requirement that may cause problems given the limits to human consciousness. In this regard, Block distinguishes between conscious experience and conscious access, and he argues that two different brain subsystems underlie the experience of being and our ability to report on that experience (2005). Moreover, accurate conscious access to all processes involved in making a choice may not even be possible because most mental processes are nonconscious and may only be inferred or observed after the fact (recall the case of blindsight). Thus, it is highly likely that subjects made errors or adjustments when they assessed the timing of their intentions. Indeed, depending on the task instructions, different areas of the brain show increases in activity and subjects misperceive events as earlier or later than they actually occur (Lau et al. 2004, 2006, 2007). Finally, simple voluntary-movement studies give instruction in advance about the action to be performed. Thus, the results suggest that the intention to act itself is likely complex and multifaceted (Gomes 1999, 2007), involving stages of planning and setting nonconscious processes in motion long before the moment of action—which means free will may be initiated long before the few seconds of experience studied in the laboratory.

Nevertheless, a wealth of evidence confirms that much human action is under nonconscious control, and that conscious experiences of intention may be manipulated to form illusions of willed action (Wegner and Wheatley 1999; Wegner 2003, 2004; Morewedge et al. 2010). Is this a problem for the Adventist, compatibilist view of free will? I do not think so. Rosenthal notes that there is no reason we must be consciously aware of our free will for free will to exist (2002)—and remember, consciousness of our consciousness is a costly extra process in a limited mind. Moreover, if human beings are indivisible entities, then any noncoerced decision between viable options, whether conscious or not, is rooted in the whole self (Rosenthal 2002; Bandura 2006; Baumeister 2008); indeed, the nonconscious processes that make many of our decisions have been shaped in part by our past conscious experience. Thus, free will may operate well in advance of the actual decision being made (Baumeister 2008)—a sensible proposition given the possible role of consciousness in mental time travel and development of future goals (Murphy 2009). In this interpretation, humans retain the freedom to prepare the kind of mind that they want to use for making decisions in the future. Free will becomes a task of character building—that is, a task of shaping the whole self: nonconscious and conscious mind, body, and spirit—through discipline. It is not just spur-of-the-moment decision making.

This compatibilist approach to free will, which recognizes that free will can be implemented in both conscious and nonconscious processes within an indivisible, material human being, is consistent with Adventist perspectives. The view that free will consists of intentions, decisions, and actions over time (as opposed to instantaneous, unrelated processes that only occur at a single point in time) mirrors the Adventist emphasis on a simple, healthful lifestyle, education across the lifespan, character building, and a habit of Sabbath observance. Moreover, Adventists have taught for over a century that free will involves voluntarily committing one's whole self to service for Christ (Tonstad 2008) with the future firmly in mind. These beliefs suggest that free will operates at the scope of a person's entire life, not merely at the scope of single finger movements. Thus, even if individuals are not consciously paying attention to how they use free will, but they use it nonetheless, they may share the experience of the people in Matthew 25 who were not aware about their own actions relative to the Judgment. Nonetheless, they were either commended for having lived holistic lives of service or judged as responsible for not having done so.

## Exploring Human Nature and Character Development

To summarize, current research in cognitive science and neuroscience strongly supports the Adventist view of human nature as an indivisible unity of mind, body, and spirit, free but limited. Furthermore, I believe that the integration of current scientific work with the biblical account of human nature suggests an additional and important principle: human beings vary in how conscious or free they are based on development, environment, and especially their own prior investment in their consciousness and free will (Bandura 2006). Biblical evidence abounds for this principle. For example, the phrase "You are blind but do not know it" is used to explain why some people do not see the real meaning of parables (Matthew 13; Mark 4; Luke 8); to establish why extraordinary events are insufficient to lead to a decision to believe the gospel (John 12; Acts 28); and to explain why people do not understand the depth of their depravity and need for salvation (Isaiah 6; Jeremiah 5; Revelation 3). Likewise, the story of Peter depicts a man who fails to exercise (or perhaps control) his will (e.g., "I will not deny you") until his discipleship is complete. Paul essentially argues this point when he says that Christians need no longer walk "darkened in their understanding" (Ephesians 4:18),[5] but instead may be "renewed" with clarity of mind (Ephesians 4:23).

Scientific support for variability in consciousness and free will comes from two lines of research in experimental social psychology that tie back into the basic neural processes discussed at the beginning of this chapter. The first line of research concerns what people *believe* about human nature. Carol Dweck and her colleagues showed that at all stages of academic development, believing that you *can* change your brain is sufficient to lead students to persist and learn; on the other hand, believing that you are determined by your circumstances of birth, genetics, and present situation leads students to give up and fail to learn and grow (Mueller and Dweck 1998; Dweck 2006). Similarly, Kathleen Vohs and Jonathan Schooler demonstrated that exposure to the ideas of determinism, which deny that people have free will, tends to make people more likely to cheat or steal in the immediate short term (2008). In both of these cases, people's *beliefs* are what matter, not whether or not they actually have free will.

The second line of research focuses on how willpower (the ability to regulate our behavior and to act on our intentions, rather than from habit or in response to stimuli—essentially, the resource that underlies free will) varies through time. In the short term, our ability to use willpower to overcome habits or to complete an effortful task is limited by the degree to which we have just used willpower for some other task (Baumeister et al. 2007; Baumeister 2008). After subjects complete a demanding task, such as trying to solve an unsolvable logic puzzle, they tend to quit earlier on the next assigned task—or to do a less complete job. Willpower, it seems, depends on the amount of glucose available in the brain in the short term (Gailliot et al. 2007; Gailliot and Baumeister 2007; Gailliot 2008). This makes sense because performing difficult tasks requires the action of more neurons, which burn up the limited supply of glucose in the brain. Because habits require less energy to produce actions (Neal et al. 2006), a depleted brain will rely more on habits than on conscious, reflective, intentional thought.

Let me be clear: consuming glucose is not the only (or best) way to improve willpower (Baumeister et al. 2007)! Over the long term, acts of

5. All Scripture quotations (unless otherwise noted) are taken from the NEW AMERICAN STANDARD BIBLE®, Copyright © 1960,1962,1963,1968,1971,1972, 1973,1975,1977,1995 by The Lockman Foundation. Used by permission.

intentional, demanding self-control strengthen self-control processes, much as exercise strengthens a muscle (Baumeister et al. 2006; Oaten and Cheng 2006). For example, tasks as simple as brushing your teeth with your non-dominant hand for a few weeks (Baumeister et al. 2006) or starting (and sticking to) an exercise program can improve self-control in other areas your life. They increase your ability to avoid negative actions, such as procrastination, and to engage in beneficial tasks, such as housecleaning (Oaten and Cheng 2006). However, you must keep challenging yourself—or your mind and body will adapt, and the effect will be lost.

Proposing that free will differs from person to person and, within individuals, from time to time, is no mere curiosity: willpower and matters of character are intimately linked. For example, depleted willpower leads people to be more aggressive and less helpful (DeWall et al. 2008; Baumeister et al. 2009); to have trouble avoiding stereotypes of others (Gailliot et al. 2007); to be more likely to be dishonest (Mead et al. 2009); to be more likely succumb to addictive behaviors (Muraven et al. 2002; Muraven et al. 2005; Vohs and Baumeister 2009); and to make more impulsive purchases (Vohs and Faber 2007). Thus, daily variations in willpower can directly affect our Christian walk. By understanding factors that shape this variability, we may consciously plan in advance to strengthen our will: by preparing good habits, taking care of our bodies, intentionally seeking our Creator, and intentionally developing our capacity for free will.

Likewise, understanding that we all do not have the same degree of willpower and are all in a process of character development might reframe our ministry to others. To begin with, the *development* of free will requires its *application* in life. Thus, a primary role for Adventist churches, schools, hospitals, families, and peers should be to build our collective capacity to exercise choice in character-building ways—not by removing all possibility of an undesired or incorrect choice, but by providing *developmentally appropriate* opportunities for the exercise of free will. Such is the approach recommended throughout the Bible, and it is not surprising that one of the fruits of the Spirit is self-control (Galatians 5:22–23). Similarly, Adventist individuals should be committed to disciplining the body, mind, and spirit in order to increase our capacity for responsible exercise of free will—because willpower (the resource necessary for free will) undergirds our ability to grow in character and in our capacity for service. (Remember: helpfulness generally decreases as willpower is depleted.) This represents, in a sense, growing your faith by your works. This view does not deny that the Holy Spirit gives strength when needed, but it is an act that human beings can take—given their free will—to be more receptive to the work of the Spirit.

In sum, meditating on the science of human nature seen through an Adventist worldview indicates the importance of integrating Adventist doctrine and practice into daily thought and life. First, rather than focusing on behaviors and beliefs as separate ideas, a holistic and humble understanding of human nature motivates the believer to seek self-discipline for the purpose of helping others. Second, a study of human nature that integrates biological and psychological accounts with the biblical record suggests a clear connection between the accounts of Creation and the Fall, which depict humans as integrated souls who used their free will to rebel against God, then to move toward Him, prompted by the gospel message of salvation.

Indeed, the developmental view of human nature that I have described encourages us to be more patient with ourselves and with each other when we make mistakes or face difficulties. If consciousness is limited by design, if free will varies by experience, and if effort is required to build character, then we should be skeptical of the empty promises of a world offering quick fixes and instant gratification, and instead be more attracted to the patient Good Shepherd who shared our experience, suffered in our stead (Isaiah 53:4–5), and offers to guide us today (Matthew 28:20).

Finally, a clear view of what Seventh-day Adventist Christians believe about human nature allows us to teach about origins, salvation, and resurrection in their proper context. God loved so deeply that He chose to live with human limitations to demonstrate dependence on the Creator, a dependence that overcame even the limitations of the grave; He loved so deeply that He sent His Son to be born helpless, to grow in favor with God and humankind, and to teach on the hillsides of Galilee. Indeed, God loved so deeply that He chose, in Christ, to demonstrate that love for all time—by forever integrating Himself into the very Creation that He spoke into being and formed with His own hands.

## Literature Cited

Aamodt, S. A. and S. Wang. 2008. Welcome to your brain: Why you lose your car keys but never forget how to drive and other puzzles of everyday life. Bloombury USA, New York.

Baddeley, A. D. 2001. Is working memory still working? American Psychologist 7:85–97.
Bandura, A. 2006. Toward a psychology of human agency. Perspectives on Psychological Science 1:164–180.
Barbur, J. L., K. H. Ruddock, and V. A. Waterfield. 1980. Human visual responses in the absence of the geniculo-calcarine projection. Brain 103:905–928.
Basinger, D. and R. Basinger. 1986. Predestination and free will: Four views of divine sovereignty and human freedom. InterVarsity Press, Downers Grove, Illinois.
Baumeister, R. F. 2008. Free will in scientific psychology. Perspectives on Psychological Science 3:14–19.
Baumeister, R. F., E. J. Masicampo, and C. N. DeWall. 2009. Prosocial benefits of feeling free: Disbelief in free will increases aggression and reduces helpfulness. Personality and Social Psychology Bulletin 35:260–268.
Baumeister, R. F., K. D. Vohs, and D. M. Tice. 2007. The strength model of self-control. Current Directions in Psychological Science 16:351–355.
Baumeister, R. F., M. Gailliot, C. N. DeWall, and M. Oaten. 2006. Self-regulation and personality: How interventions increase regulatory success, and how depletion moderates the effects of traits on behavior. Journal of Personality 74:1773–1801.
Beauregard, M. 2007. Mind does really matter: Evidence from neuroimaging studies of emotional self-regulation, psychotherapy, and placebo effect. Progress in Neurobiology 81:218–236.
Bechtel, W. 1994. Levels of description and explanation in cognitive science. Minds and Machines 4:1–25.
Beilock, S. L. and T. H. Carr. 2005. When high-powered people fail: Working memory and "choking under pressure" in math. Psychological Science 16:101–105.
Block, N. 2005. Two neural correlates of consciousness. Trends in Cognitive Sciences 9:46–52.
Bloom, P. 2004. Descartes' baby: How the science of child development explains what makes us human. Basic Books, New York.
Botzung, A., E. Denkova, and L. Manning. 2008. Experiencing past and future events: Functional neuroimaging evidence on the neural basis of mental time travel. Brain and Cognition 66:202–212.

Boyd, G. A. and P. R. Eddy. 2009. Across the spectrum: Understanding issues in evangelical theology. Baker Academic, Grand Rapids, MI.

Bridge, H., O. Thomas, S. Jbabdi, and A. Cowey. 2008. Changes in connectivity after visual cortical brain damage underlie altered vision. Brain 131:1433–1444.

Brown, W., N. Murphy, and H. N. Malony. 1998. Whatever happened to the soul? Scientific and theological portraits of human nature. Fortress Press, Minneapolis.

Cowey, A. 2004. Fact, artifact, and myth about blindsight. Quarterly Journal of Experimental Psychology 57A:577–609.

Cranford, R. 2005. Facts, lies, and videotapes: The permanent vegetative state and the sad case of Terri Schiavo. Journal of Law, Medicine, & Ethics 33:363–371.

Crick, F. 1994. The astonishing hypothesis. Scribner, New York.

Crick, F. and C. Koch. 2003. A framework for consciousness. Nature Neuroscience 6:119–126.

Dehaene, S. and L. Naccache. 2001. Towards a cognitive neuroscience of consciousness: Basic evidence and a workspace framework. Cognition 79:1–37.

DeWall, C. N., R. F. Baumeister, M. T. Gailliot, and J. K. Maner. 2008. Depletion makes the heart grow less helpful: Helping as a function of self-regulatory energy and genetic relatedness. Personality and Social Psychology Bulletin 34:1653–1662.

Donohoe, R. T. and D. Benton. 1999. Cognitive functioning is susceptible to the level of blood glucose. Psychopharmacology 145:378–385.

Dunning, D. 2005. Self-Insight: Roadblocks and detours on the path to knowing thyself. Psychology Press, New York.

Dweck, C. S. 2006. Mindset: The new psychology of success. Random House, New York.

Eagleman, D. M. and T. J. Sejnowski. 2000. Motion integration and postdiction in visual awareness. Science 287:2036–2038.

Edelman, G. M. and G. Tononi. 2001. A universe of consciousness: How matter becomes imagination. Basic Books, New York.

Fields, R. D. 2004. The other half of the brain. Scientific American 290(4):54–61.

Gailliot, M. T. 2008. Unlocking the energy dynamics of executive functioning: Linking executive functioning to brain glycogen. Perspectives

on Psychological Science 3:245–263.
Galliot, M. T. and R. F. Baumeister. 2007. The physiology of willpower: Linking blood glucose to self-control. Personality and Social Psychology Review 11:303–327.
Gailliot, M. T. et al. 2007. Self-control relies on glucose as a limited energy source: Willpower is more than a metaphor. Journal of Personality and Social Psychology 92:325–336.
Gomes, G. 1999. Volition and the readiness potential. Journal of Consciousness Studies 6:59–76.
Gomes, G. 2007. Free will, the self, and the brain. Behavioral Sciences and the Law 25:221–234.
Goodale, M. A., A. D. Milner, L. S. Jakobson, and D. P. Carey. 1991. A neurological dissociation between perceiving objects and grasping them. Nature 349:154–156.
Goodwin, C. J. 1999. A history of modern psychology. Wiley, New York.
Goswami, U. 2006. Neuroscience and education: From research to practice? Nature Reviews Neuroscience 7:406–413.
Greenfield, S. A. and T. F. T. Collins. 2005. A neuroscientific approach to consciousness. Progress in Brain Research 150:586–587.
Hameroff, S. and R. Penrose. 2003. Conscious events as orchestrated space-time selections. NeuroQuantology 1:10–35.
Hubbard, E. M. and V. S. Ramachandran. 2005. Neurocognitive mechanisms of synesthesia. Neuron 48:509–520.
Kadosh, R. C., A. Henik, A. Catena, V. Walsh, and L. J. Fuentes. 2009. Induced cross-modal synaesthetic experience without abnormal neuronal connections. Psychological Science 20:258–265.
Klawans, J. 2009. Josephus on fate, free will, and ancient Jewish types of compatibilism. Numen 56:44–90.
Koch, C. 2004. The quest for consciousness: A neurobiological approach. Roberts and Company, Englewood, Colorado.
Koch, C. and K. Hepp. 2006. Quantum mechanics in the brain. Nature 440:611–612.
Kornhuber, H. H., and L. Deecke. 1965. Hirnpotentialänderungen bei Willkürbewegungen und passive Bewegungen des Menschen: Bereitschaftspotential und reafferente Potentiale. Pflügers Archiv für Gesamte Physiologie 284:1–17.
Kouider, S. 2009. Neurobiological theories of consciousness. Pp. 87–100

in W. Banks, ed. Encyclopedia of consciousness. Elsevier, New York.

Kuntaraf, J. O. and K. Liwidjaja-Kuntaraf. 2008. Emphasizing the wholeness of man. Journal of the Adventist Theological Society 19:109–136.

Lamprecht, R. and J. LeDoux. 2004. Structural plasticity and memory. Nature Reviews Neuroscience 5:45–54.

Lau, H. C., R. D. Rogers, P. Haggard, and R. E. Passingham. 2004. Attention to intention. Science 303:1208–1209.

Lau, H. C., R. D. Rogers, and R. E. Passingham. 2006. On measuring the perceived onsets of spontaneous actions. Journal of Neuroscience 26:7265–7271.

Lau, H. C., R. D. Rogers, and R. E. Passingham. 2007. Manipulating the experiences onset of intention after action execution. Journal of Cognitive Neuroscience 19:81–90.

Libet, B. 1999. Do we have free will? Journal of Consciousness Studies 6:47–57.

Libet, B., C. A. Gleason, E. W. Wright, and D. K. Pearly. 1983. Time of conscious intention to act in relation to onset of cerebral activity readiness-potential: The unconscious initiation of a freely voluntary act. Brain 106:623–642.

Lilienfeld, S. O., S. J. Lynn, J. Ruscio, and B. L. Beyerstein. 2010. 50 great myths of popular psychology: Shattering widespread misconceptions about human behavior. Wiley-Blackwell, Chichester, United Kingdom.

Lombardi, W. J., E. T. Higgins, and J. A. Bargh. 1987. The role of consciousness in priming effects on categorization: Assimilation versus contrast as a function of the awareness of the priming task. Personality and Social Psychology Bulletin 13:411–429.

McCabe, D. P. and A. D. Castel. 2008. Seeing is believing: The effect of brain images on judgments of scientific reasoning. Cognition 107:343–352.

McGovern, K. and B. J. Baars. 2007. Cognitive theories of consciousness. Pp. 177–205 in P. D. Zelazo, M. Moscovitch, and E. Thompson, eds. The Cambridge handbook of consciousness. Cambridge University Press, Cambridge, United Kingdom.

Mead, N. L., R. F. Baumeister, F. Gino, M. E. Schweitzer, and D. Ariely. 2009. Too tired to tell the truth: Self-Control resource depletion and dishonesty. Journal of Experimental Social Psychology 45:594–597.

Miller, A. G. 2004. The social psychology of good and evil. Guilford, New York.
Monti, M. M. et al. 2010. Willful modulation of brain activity in disorders of consciousness. The New England Journal of Medicine 362:579–589.
Morewedge, C. K., K. Gray, and D. M. Wegner. 2010. Perish the forethought: Premeditation engenders misperceptions of personal control. Pp. 260–278 in R. Hassan, K. Ochsner, and Y. Trope, eds. Self-control in brain, mind, and society. Oxford University Press, New York.
Morse, S. J. 2008. Determinism and the death of folk psychology: Two challenges to responsibility from neuroscience. Minnesota Journal of Law, Science, and Technology 9:1–36.
Mueller, C. M. and C. S. Dweck. 1998. Praise for intelligence can undermine children's motivation and performance. Journal of Personality and Social Psychology 75:33–52.
Muraven, M., R. L. Collins, and K. Nienhaus. 2002. Self-control and alcohol restraint: An initial application of the self-control strength model. Psychology of Addictive Behaviors 16:113–120.
Muraven, M., R. L. Collins, S. Shiffman, and J. A. Paty. 2005. Daily fluctuations in self-control demands and alcohol intake. Psychology of Addictive Behaviors 19:140–147.
Murphy, N. 2009. Introduction and overview. Pp. 1–28 in N. Murphy, G. F. R. Ellis, and T. O'Connor, eds. Downward causation and the neurobiology of freewill. Springer-Verlag, Berlin.
Nagel, T. 1974. What is it like to be a bat? Philosophical Review 83:435–450.
Neal, D. T., W. Wood, and J. M. Quinn. 2006. Habits—a repeat performance. Current Directions in Psychological Science 15:198–202.
Oaten, M. and K. Cheng. 2006. Longitudinal gains in self-regulation from regular physical exercise. British Journal of Health Psychology 11:717–733.
Owen, A. M., M. R. Coleman, M. Boly, M. H. Davis, S. Laureys, and J. D. Pickard. 2006. Detecting awareness in the vegetative state. Science 313:1402.
Peterson, G. R. 2003. Minding God: Theology and the cognitive sciences. Fortress Press, Minneapolis.
Picirilli, R. E. 2002. Grace, faith, free will. Contrasting views of salvation: Calvinism and Arminianism. Randall House, Nashville, Tennessee.
Pinker, S. 1999. How the mind works. W. W. Norton, New York.

Poldrack, R. A., Y. O. Halchenko, and S. J. Hanson. 2009. Decoding the large-scale structure of brain function by classifying mental states across individuals. Psychological Science 20:1364–1372.

Popper, K. and J. C. Eccles. 1983. The self and its brain: An argument for interactionism. Routledge, London.

Posner, M. I. and M. K. Rothbart. 1998. Attention, self-regulation, and consciousness. Philosophical Transactions of the Royal Society of London B 353:1915–1927.

Principe, G. F., T. Kanaya, S. J. Ceci, and M. Singh. 2006. Believing is seeing: How rumors can engender false memories in preschoolers. Psychological Science 17:243–248.

Rabbitt, P. 2002. Consciousness is slower than you think. Quarterly Journal of Experimental Psychology 55A:1081–1092.

Ramachandran, V. S. 2004. A brief tour of human consciousness. Pi Press, New York.

Ramachandran, V. S. and S. Blakeslee. 1998. Phantoms in the brain: Probing the mysteries of the human mind. William Morrow, New York.

Ringo, J. L., R. W. Doty, S. Demeter, and P. Y. Simard. 1994. Time is of the essence: A conjecture that hemispheric specialization arises from interhemispheric conduction delay. Cerebral Cortex 4:331–343.

Rosenthal, D. M. 2002. The timing of conscious states. Consciousness and Cognition 11:215–220.

Schacter, D. L. 2001. The seven sins of memory: How the mind forgets and remembers. Houghton Mifflin, Boston.

Soon, C. S., M. Brass, H.-J. Heinze, and J. D. Haynes. 2008. Unconscious determinants of free decisions in the human brain. Nature Neuroscience 11:543–545.

Suddendorf, T. and J. Busby. 2005. Making decisions with the future in mind: Developmental and comparative identification of mental time travel. Learning and Motivation 36:110–125.

Tononi, G. 2004. An information integration theory of consciousness. BMC Neuroscience 5:42

Tononi, G. and C. Koch. 2008. The neural correlates of consciousness: An update. Annals of the New York Academy of Sciences 1124:239–261.

Tonstad, S. K. 2008. The message of the trees in the midst of the garden. Journal of the Adventist Theological Society 19:82–97.

Velmans, M. 2009. Understanding consciousness. Routledge, London.

Vohs, K. D. and J. W. Schooler. 2008. The value of believing in free will. Psychological Science 19:49–54.

Vohs, K. D., and R. F. Baumeister. 2009. Addiction and free will. Addiction Research Theory 17:231–235.

Vohs, K. D. and R. J. Faber. 2007. Spent resources: Self-Regulatory resource availability affects impulse buying. Journal of Consumer Research 33:537–547.

Wade, K. A., M. Garry, J. D. Read, and D. S. Lindsay. 2002. A picture is worth a thousand lies: Using false photographs to create false childhood memories. Psychonomic Bulletin and Review 9:597–603.

Wang, S. et al. 2008. Functional trade-offs in white matter axonal scaling. Journal of Neuroscience 28:4047–4056.

Ward, J. 2006. The student's guide to cognitive neuroscience. Psychology Press, New York.

Wegner, D. M. 2003. The mind's best trick: How we experience conscious will. Trends in Cognitive Sciences 7:65–69.

Wegner, D. M. 2004. Précis of The illusion of conscious will. Behavioral and Brain Sciences 27:649–659.

Wegner, D. M. and T. Wheatley. 1999. Apparent mental causation: Sources of the experience of will. American Psychologist 54:480–492.

Weisberg, D. S. 2008. Caveat lector: The presentation of neuroscience information in the popular media. Scientific Review of Mental Health Practice 6:51–56.

Weisberg, D. S., F. C. Keil, J. Goodstein, E. Rawson, and J. R. Gray. 2008. The seductive allure of neuroscience explanations. Journal of Cognitive Neuroscience 20:470–477.

Weiskrantz, L., E. K. Warrington, M. D. Sanders, and J. Marshall. 1974. Visual capacity in the hemianopic field following a restricted occipital ablation. Brain 97:709–728.

Wheeler, M. A., D. T. Stuss, and E. Tulving. 1997. Toward a theory of episodic memory: The frontal lobes and autonoetic consciousness. Psychological Bulletin 121:331–354.

Wilson, E. O. 1975/2000. Sociobiology: The new synthesis. Harvard University Press, Cambridge, Massachusetts.

Zimbardo, P. G. 2008. The Lucifer effect: Understanding how good people turn evil. Random House, New York.

# Chapter Four

# THE SCOPE AND LIMITS OF THE EVOLUTIONARY PROCESS

**Leonard Brand**

Imagine a conversation among three people who have been thinking new thoughts about the living world. Edward insists, "You have twisted my theory into a magician's game with nature." "No," retorts Charles, "Alfred here is the one who wants to turn a magician loose in the garden." Alfred responds, "You are both partly right, but you, Charles, want to ignore the facts and claim more for natural selection than the evidence allows."

Edward Blyth had published his theory of natural selection as a conserving process that limits the damaging aspects of genetic change, eliminating the weaker individuals, but with no ability to make a new type of animal (Lester and Bohlin 1989). Charles Darwin apparently was influenced by Blyth's theory (Eiseley 1979), but Darwin proposed that natural selection is also creative, selecting advantageous new variations in the process of evolving the entire living world from simple beginnings (1859). Alfred Russell Wallace independently developed a theory that agreed with Darwin's version of evolution, up to a point. Darwin and Wallace parted company when it came to the origin of the human brain and the possible involvement of a Creator. Wallace, in contrast to Darwin, had spent a great deal of time studying life in the tropics, living side by side with the human races of the equatorial regions. Darwin and many of his fellow British biologists believed those "primitive" races in the tropics were advanced only a little beyond the apes, but Wallace's experience with them told a different story. Wallace knew those so-called primitive races were no less intelligent than any other race, and he did not believe that evolution could produce a brain with abilities so far beyond the simple necessities of life. He believed there had to be divine involvement in the origin of the human brain (Eiseley 1955; chapter 4 in Gould 1980). That idea was anathema to Darwin. In this chapter we will pursue these questions: What is the theory of evolution? What can evolution do? Does it have limits? And lastly, who was right—Blyth, Darwin, or Wallace?

## Science, Philosophy, and Faith

In modern culture it is common to claim that science uses neutral, unbiased methods to discover objective facts, while religion is only the realm of personal, subjective values. In this worldview, science with its facts is the realm of the mind, and religion with only assumptions and values is the realm of the emotions. However, there is no such thing as an objective, value-free search for truth. Everyone works within some worldview, with its accompanying assumptions. Every system of thought, every worldview, is based on some ultimate principle that is accepted by faith (in contrast to accepting it because of convincing evidence). Most scientists accept the secular worldview, based on the principle of naturalistic materialism, which is accepted by faith, and all scientific data on origins are interpreted according to that principle. The religious worldview that accepts a literal, recent Creation is based on the principle that God has involved Himself in supernatural ways in the origin of the universe and of life and has communicated this to us, and this is accepted by faith in God and the Bible (Pearcey 2005).

The aim of this entire discussion is not to prove whether Creation or large-scale evolution is true. That is not a realistic goal for science or for religion. The aim is to compare a few important aspects of how each worldview deals with the evidence currently available to us, and how well these worldviews answer the most important questions about our existence and destiny.

## The Origin of Life

Before there can be evolution there must be living organisms to evolve, so we will discuss the origin of life first. Darwin and his British colleagues thought that a cell is a bit of gel-like protoplasm surrounded by a membrane—a simple structure that could easily evolve. More recent scientific advances have demolished this view by revealing how complex a living cell is, thus making it more difficult to explain how the first life forms originated. Answers we give to that question will fall primarily into one of two categories: either life originated by itself, merely from the action of the laws of chemistry and physics (abiogenesis), or it was invented and made by an intelligent designer. Later in this chapter we will consider the possible combination of these two—evolution and intelligent design—working together.

Life is a unique and unlikely phenomenon. Many other things, such as rocks, minerals, crystals, water and other fluids, and snowflakes, will form spontaneously if the conditions are correct, in accordance with the laws of chemistry and physics. But life is very different. Life certainly depends on the existence of matter and on the laws of chemistry and physics, but matter and the laws that govern it are not sufficient to explain life's origins or continued existence. The laws of chemistry and physics only provide a set of conditions that allow life to exist. They are like the ground upon which a house can be built. But the ground does not make a house, and the laws of nature do not make life. There is something beyond those laws that makes a house, and likewise there is something else that makes life. It is not possible to determine a set of conditions that are sufficient to produce life, because the essence of life consists of something unique and different from any of the raw materials. Life can be compared with the book you are reading. The book's pages no doubt contain some chemicals that will form if the conditions are right. But the book would be meaningless without the one constituent that also defines life: information (see chapter 2).

Let us briefly return to the house analogy. The laws of nature produce iron, gypsum, copper, and the constituents of concrete, but they have no ability to know how to put those together to make a house. God made an exquisite set of laws of nature and uses those laws to operate His universe. But those exquisite laws will never know what a bedroom is for, or how to design one. That depends on an intelligent agent, one who can invent the concept of *house* and figure out how to design one so it is functional. A blueprint exists because someone invented it and put it down on paper.

The information that sustains life is conveyed by specific sequences of subunits within DNA, RNA, and proteins (Fig. 1)—directly comparable to human writing, which conveys information in sequences of letters, words, and sentences. The laws of chemistry and physics do not specify whether *E* will come before *H,* and likewise they do not specify the sequences of subunits in DNA or proteins. We know that human writing conveys information that someone organized, and it seems reasonable to infer the same for the information within DNA and proteins.

If life arose without a designer, where did the information so central to life come from? That is the challenge for abiogenesis. Some simple biological molecules, such as amino acids, will form spontaneously if the conditions are right. However, amino acids are only like bricks, and bricks alone do not make a house. There must be instructions for arranging the bricks (and many other structures) into a functional house. Similarly, there must also be instructions on how to arrange the amino acids to make a great variety of functional proteins. The amino acid sequence in a protein

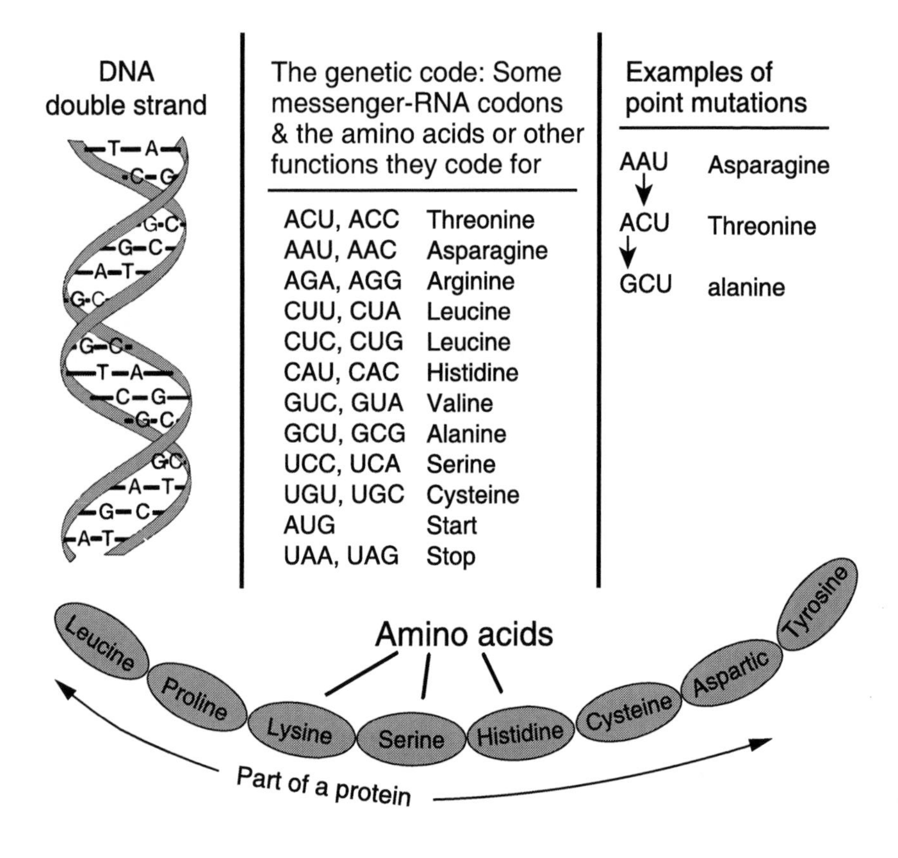


**Figure 1**—Left: The structure of DNA, with its pairs of bases (adenine [*A*], guanine [*G*], cytosine [*C*], and thymine [*T*]) between the two strands of the double helix. *T* always pairs with *A,* and *C* always pairs with *G.* Middle: A sample of messenger-RNA codons (codon=a sequence of three bases that codes for a specific amino acid, or indicates start or stop the construction of a protein). Note that uracil [*U*] replaces *T* in RNA. Right: Sample of point mutations that change one base and result in a different amino acid. Lower: A portion of a representative protein, composed of a chain of amino acids.

determines whether the protein will be a muscle fiber, make copies of DNA, or be entirely useless.

The amino acid bricks combine in the right sequences to form biomolecular machines. Cells are alive in part because of the biochemical activities of thousands of protein biomolecular machines. They convert energy into usable forms, synthesize proteins (in ribosomes) as specified by the information in DNA, eliminate waste, distribute food materials as needed, and produce new cells. The first cells would not be alive until they contained all the components to maintain this integrated suite of biochemical life processes. And that is not all. Just having the right molecules does not make something alive. The difference between a dead cell and a live cell is that in the live cell the biochemical processes have been set in motion. How would that happen spontaneously?

In summary, the challenge for any theory about the origin of life is to explain the simultaneous origin of all these biomolecular machines that cooperate harmoniously in supporting life, along with the DNA information system with its instructions for making and controlling the entire system. This is comparable to the origin of the concept of *house,* the blueprints in all their details, and all the complex parts needed to make the house.

A variety of scenarios seek to explain how life supposedly arose spontaneously. One proposal is that life began not with proteins, but with RNA. Since RNA can act as a catalyst as well as carry information, this RNA World-origin concept suggests that RNA-based life arose first and later was converted to our present DNA/RNA/protein system. Another theory suggests that life arose when protobiological molecules adhered to clay templates, facilitating their concentration into a functioning system. There are other scenarios as well, but all have the same fundamental weakness: none of them answer the question of how biological information came to be. Those scenarios provide conditions that might allow certain bricks (simple organic compounds) to form, or that will speed up biochemical reactions, but they do not explain the origin of the necessary sequence of subunits of DNA and proteins that compose biological information. Consequently such scenarios offer no potential for explaining how life could begin without a designer.

One could suggest that natural selection is the factor needed to assist the origin of life processes. However, natural selection could not have any influence on the process until organisms existed, alive and replicating, with a genetic system controlling the characteristics that natural selection could act upon.

Some argue that given enough time it is likely that the biological information just happened to come together by blind chance to make life (e.g., Dawkins 1986, 1996). This approach relies on faith that such a process would actually work. Some have calculated the probability of this happening. All such probabilities that I have seen leave out a critical set of factors—all the chemical and physical hazards in nature that tend to destroy, rather than construct, large biological molecules if they are not in the protective environment of a living cell.

These theories of life's origins are not issues subject to scientific proof. However, the most consistent explanation of the scientific evidence seems to be another faith-based option: the biological information in the first living things had to be invented, designed by a superintelligent, mathematically oriented scientific genius of a Creator (see Thaxton et al. 1984; Meyer 2009).

## Evolution: Mutation and Natural Selection

The same biological information required for the origin of life is also key to understanding changes in organisms once life came into existence. Each living organism contains an instruction manual, with all the information needed for its embryological development and growth to maturity. That information must define what its structure and functioning will be, and even some of the information it will need to guide its behavior in a successful life. In Darwin's day nothing was known about this instruction manual, but since the mid-20th century we have known its location is in the DNA of each cell.

The biochemical mechanisms that allow each cell of the body to read the instruction manual also provide for changes that will assist the species in adapting to changing environmental conditions. In this chapter we will not try to provide a comprehensive summary of this topic, as space is limited and other sources are available for that purpose (see Roth 1998; Meyer et al. 2007; Brand 2006a, 2009, and literature cited there). We will only discuss the concepts necessary to understand the nature of evolution and to evaluate the strengths and limits of the process.

Evolutionary changes begin with mutations: changes to the sequence of bases in a DNA strand. The interested reader may consult a good general biology or genetics text for a thorough review of mutations, but for our purposes here, we will review a couple of key concepts about them. First, mutations are thought to be random with respect to the needs of an organism; the mutation process does not know what the organism needs (or will need in the future). Second, the vast majority of mutations are either neutral (that is, they do not affect the ability of the organism to survive and reproduce) or negative. This accords with our experience: any time you randomly change letters or words in a book, the result is likely to either make no difference, or else to mess up the meaning of a word or sentence.

Occasionally, however, a mutation might occur that accidently benefits an organism, perhaps by slightly altering one of its proteins in a way that enhances the protein's function. Since the probability of those helpful mutations is extremely low, this may seem to be an unlikely mechanism for evolving more complex organisms. To be fair it must be remembered that mutation is only the first step. The next step is natural selection.

Imagine that you and a friend come face to face with an angry, hungry grizzly bear. If one of you is a fast runner and the other is walking with crutches, which one of you is more likely to live to have children? There is a joke that you do not have to be able to outrun a bear—you just have to outrun one member of your hiking group. That is not, of course, a very altruistic viewpoint, but it is natural selection, pure and simple. There are many more animals born or hatched than the earth could support, and natural selection is a nonrandom process that determines which ones will survive and reproduce.

Mutations and recombinations of genetic features at reproduction result in considerable variation in a population of organisms. Some individuals will have characteristics more favorable to survival than other individuals. These favored individuals are more likely to survive and leave successful offspring, and consequently their genetic traits will be more common in the next generation. This is the process of natural selection, which is not random, but favors individuals that are better suited to their environment.

The process of natural selection was not adequately understood until the mid-19th century, but it actually is not a difficult or controversial concept. It is quite logical that faster antelopes will outrun more cheetahs, and that rabbits with camouflaged fur colors will be overlooked by more hawks. That is natural selection. It is a simple and straightforward description of a process that happens all the time. Darwin and others of his era began to understand how many excess offspring many animals produce, and to understand that natural selection determines which of these individuals will survive to produce the next generation.

The real question is not, Does natural selection happen? It does. The more important question is, Can random (nondirected) mutations provide the raw material (new information) for natural selection to act on in order to produce something new? Part of the answer is fairly clear and is recognized by most scientists, whether they believe in Creation or not. We will discuss this concept and then address some more controversial issues.

## Levels of Evolutionary Change

For several years I spent part of my time following chipmunks through forest and sagebrush, seeking to understand their behavior and how it differs among species. It was a rewarding experience, even though chipmunks can be frustratingly secretive. There are 13 species of chipmunks in California, each species occupying its chosen niche within a specific geographical area. What are the possible explanations for the origin of these species and their characteristics? One possibility is that God created each species just like it is now (fixity of species) in its current geographical range. In Darwin's time and before, this was the most common explanation. In the 18th and 19th centuries several biologists began to doubt this story. Some of them moved toward the theory that God had provided plants and animals with the potential for change within each created group of organisms, and through time these changes resulted in new species, different enough to be placed in new genera or maybe even new families (Landgren 1993). The most well-known advocate of this concept was Carolus Linnaeus, the father of modern taxonomy. He is at times portrayed as an advocate of the fixity of species. Linnaeus apparently started his career with that belief, but he gradually recognized evidence for more change, finally advocating that new types had developed within created groups, up to the level of new families (Landgren 1993). Charles Darwin's writings do not indicate that he was aware of this trend.

During that same time, others also saw evidence of change through time but did not include God or Creation as part of the theories they developed about origins. They may have had some belief in God, but they did not include Him in their theories. Several persons proposed evolutionary theories before Charles Darwin, and they contributed concepts that were important background for Darwin's thinking (Bowler 1990). We will focus, however, on Darwin's theory and its development since its original publication (Darwin 1859).

Darwin became convinced that the process of natural selection will result in new adaptations to changing environments. Other biologists later realized that if these changes result in a population that is unable to successfully breed with another, related population, the result is a new species. Speciation is not really a unique process; it is just what naturally results if selection makes two populations different in a some way that blocks successful reproduction between them.

Furthermore, Darwin proposed that when natural selection continued for a sufficiently long time, minor changes would accumulate more changes until new biological structures and new body types result (examples of body types: mammals, worms, and starfish). He believed that the long-term result has been the evolution of all types of living organisms from a common ancestor. Most evolutionary biologists today accept that same concept.

Changes resulting from mutation and natural selection can be put in several categories (Fig. 2). Genetic changes within a species are *microevolution.* If the very same process of mutation and natural selection produces a new species, this is speciation. *Macroevolution* includes speciation and changes above the species level. However, I will not use this term for a couple of reasons. For one thing, *macroevolution* is not always defined consistently, at times resulting in confusion. In addition, the same process of mutation and natural selection responsible for changes within species (microevolution) also result in new genera (macroevolution). Thus the same mechanism is involved in microevolution and in the lower levels of macroevolution.

The bigger, critical question for biology is whether mutation and natural selection are able to produce new gene complexes, new kinds of structures, and new types of organisms. Another term, *megaevolution* (Simpson 1944), describes this level of change—evolution of new orders, classes, and phyla. *Megaevolution* has not gained wide usage in the evolutionary literature, but I will employ it in this essay because it is a more useful term than *macroevolution*. Megaevolution, if it occurs, involves the evolution of new biological information; new gene complexes, new kinds of structures, and/or new physiological systems. We will return to this question later.

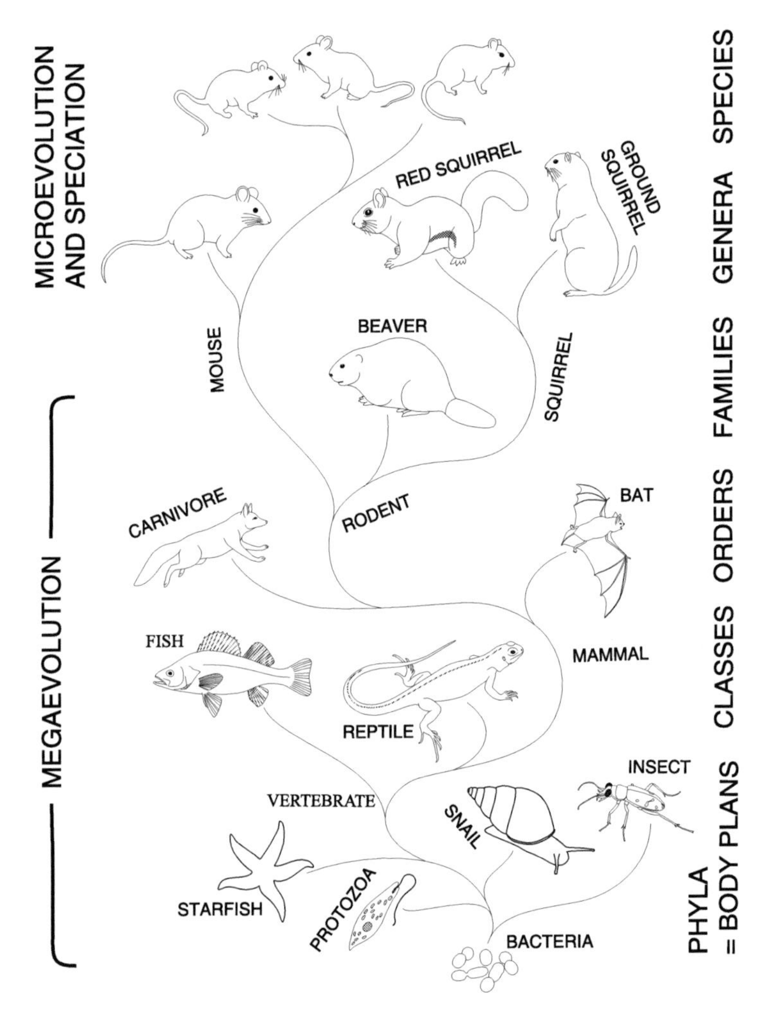


**Figure 2**—A phylogenetic tree with representative animals to illustrate the systematic categories of phyla, classes, and so on. Adapted from figure 5.1 in Leonard Brand and David C. Jarnes, *Beginnings: Are Science and Scripture Partners in the Search for Origins?* (Nampa, ID: Pacific Press Publishing Association, 2005), 45. Used by permission. *Body plan* is a term that refers to the basic pattern of body parts of an animal (e.g., insects with external, jointed skeleton; vertebrate with internal skeleton). Each class contains one or more orders; each order contains one or more families, and so on. Evolution of orders (maybe families) or higher categories from a common ancestor represents megaevolution, while biological change within a species is microevolution, and speciation is the origin of a new species. This process may make sufficient change so the animal is called a new genus, but this is not necessarily a process different from microevolution.

## Interpretations Supporting Megaevolution and Common Ancestry, and Some Responses

Let us look more closely at representative arguments for megaevolution, and/or for common ancestry of all forms of life. Of the wide range of arguments used in support of megaevolution and common ancestry of all life (e.g., Ayala 2006; Coyne 2009; Brand 2009; and literature cited therein), we will discuss several of the most pertinent ones.

### *Universal Biochemical Homologies*

A common argument made for universal common ancestry is that biochemical similarities across almost all life forms indicate that they evolved from one common ancestor. For example, almost all living things have the same genetic code, based on DNA and RNA, and evolutionists argue that these deeply shared features were inherited from their last common ancestor. However, features shared by essentially all life forms, such as DNA, RNA, or other biochemical systems, could theoretically have arisen by either common descent or common design, and the evidence in itself does not tell us which explanation is correct. The same is true for other features shared across animal groups, such as the internal skeletal structure of vertebrates.

### *A Possibility: The Evolution of Complexity*

The origin of complex eyes has a long history as a classic argument over what evolution can do. Creationists argue that evolution cannot produce something so complex as an eye. But can such a complex organ be produced by mutation and selection? The probability of it happening seems extremely low. On the other side, however, there are a variety of eyes and light-sensitive structures in many different animals. These can be lined up in order, from very simple light-sensitive eyespots to the most complex vertebrate eyes, and other eyes exhibit intermediate levels of complexity. It thus does not appear so difficult to evolve from one to the next. The changes between them do not appear to be very great. Richard Dawkins uses an analogy for this process. Climbing up the vertical face of a mountain is, for many of us, an unlikely task. However, it may be possible to climb up the gently sloping back side of the mountain with ease (Dawkins 1996). This is analogous to evolving an eye by many small steps between the different types of existing eyes. One suggested mechanism is that proteins or complexes of proteins evolve to form a simpler eye or for some other function, and then when these parts are already present in the organism, duplicate copies can be produced and co-opted for use in making a complex eye. Some authors claim that analogies like this are adequate to eliminate the need for intelligent design (Young and Edis 2004).

In response to this nice just-so story, we must ask, Will the proposed mechanism overcome the obstacles to evolving that complex eye? When you were younger, you perhaps played with Lego bricks. Simple bricks could be fitted together to make anything from a car to a skyscraper. Is that analogous to the co-option of biological parts to make a complex eye? The problem here is that the Lego bricks were carefully engineered, designed with predetermined building goals. Natural selection is strictly short-sighted: it cannot plan ahead. It has no way to design something to provide for a future use. Natural selection cannot plan ahead and design eyespots for the reason of later combining them with other parts to make a more complex eye. This makes the co-option idea rather unlikely, probably no more likely than making the complex eye from scratch. The co-option of parts for a new use would not just mean fitting them together to make something new. It would involve much re-engineering of parts so that they could work together for the new use, along with production of a complex of regulatory genes to guide the process of making appropriate quantities of each part and fitting those parts together. Before the story of "climbing up the mountain" from simple eyespots to a complex eye can be seriously considered, its proponents will need to demonstrate that the long series of sophisticated biochemical changes along the way could actually happen without intelligent guidance.

Complex camera-type eyes exist in squids and in vertebrates (Gould 1994). This fact multiplies the statistical difficulties involved in making such eyes, because they would have to evolve more than once—independently. Is it realistic to think this will happen, not only with camera-type eyes, but also with many other structures that face the same problem? That depends on how much confidence we have in the process of mutation and natural selection.

### *Animal Structures—Ancestry or Design?*

Another common type of anti-Creation reasoning can be illustrated by evolutionary claims related to the wings of bats. The evolutionary process, as generally understood, can only evolve structures that can develop from the raw material an organism's ancestors provided. If bats evolved from other mammals that already had the mammalian forelimb bone structure, bats were constrained to make wings by elongating the fingers to make a hand-like wing. Evolution could not produce a more creative design, uniquely suited for a bat, as we would expect an intelligent designer to do.

This basic argument is often used in a variety of situations. It is often claimed that an intelligent God, an omniscient Designer, would never make organisms the way they are (Ayala 2006). This argument depends, however, on the assumption that we know what God would do. Is that a safe assumption? Maybe it is. Maybe God would not do it that way. But how would we know with any certainty? If we are willing to consider the possibility that there is a divine Creator, we will have to study nature to determine how He would design things. The evidence tells us that if there is a Designer, He created a set of basic designs for each group of organisms, and then modified these designs for the needs of each creature in that group. Human designers and engineers do this all the time, so why would an intelligent God not do the same? Those who have studied bats extensively have found that a bat's dexterous, hand-like wing is ideally suited for its lifestyle. To make such a highly efficient wing design using the same kind of bones found in a mouse's limb seems very creative indeed.

### *Phylogeny*

The phylogeny of a group of organisms is the presumed pathway of their evolution from a common ancestor, often represented by a phylogenetic tree (Fig. 2). The scientific literature contains many phylogenetic trees (one type is called a cladogram); some represent microevolution and speciation (also accepted by creationists) and some represent evolution of major groups (megaevolution). When these trees appear in scientific publications, we tend to assume that all these evolutionary events happened, but such is not the case. To understand why, we need to consider how these trees are generated.

In producing a phylogenetic tree, a systematist gathers data on the species to be studied. Such data could include behavioral, physiological, morphological, and/or biochemical attributes of all species under study. Using complex computer programs, systematists then analyze the data and identify one or more phylogenetic trees that best explain the presumed evolution of these attributes. By placing the attributes on this phylogenetic tree, systematists thus can infer when during the presumed evolutionary process each new feature first appeared.

The main issue to keep in mind is that this process, as it is used by almost all scientists, is not designed to ask whether the groups of organisms most likely originated through evolution from a common ancestor, or through separate creation events. Origin by evolution is assumed, and thus the process of phylogenetic analysis does not tell us whether or not any of the organisms originated by separate creation of basic groups followed by subsequent microevolution and speciation within each group. Because it is based on the assumption of megevolution, the existence of phylogenetic trees does not answer our question whether megaevolution is genetically possible.

*Suboptimal Designs: An Argument for Evolution*

Are biological structures ideally designed, or are they less-than-ideal results of evolutionary processes? We can begin this discussion by illustrating it with a related issue, the existence of vestigial structures. These structures, believed to have been useful in an ancient ancestors, are still present but thought to no longer be useful in their modern descendents (at least not in the same way). In 1895, one publication listed about 80 vestigial structures in humans—structures thought to be remnants of our evolutionary history that are no longer useful (Wiedershiem 1895). The list included the thyroid, thymus, pituitary, and the middle ear! We laugh at that list now, but it was treated seriously in 1895. This line of reasoning, based on the idea that some structure has no (or a reduced) function or represents a poor design, is always going to be a weak argument. We never know when new research will reveal the function of an organ that we did not know about before. If we want to avoid looking uninformed in a few decades, it is probably best to avoid any claims about poor design or lack of function. The eye has given us an excellent modern illustration of that caution.

It has often been claimed that the vertebrate eye represents a poor design that an intelligent designer would not use. This claim arises because as the light enters the vertebrate eye it has to go through several layers of neural cells before reaching the photoreceptors that actually form the visual image. Certainly an intelligent supernatural designer would put the photoreceptors in front of the other cell layers, for efficient light reception! The backward retina is pictured as a cobbled-together evolutionary structure, whereas any good human engineer would have made a better design.

Recent research shows that this claim is uninformed. Researchers discovered that one type of cell found throughout the retina has a remarkable and previously unknown function. These cells are living optical fibers that carry the light through the layers of neural cells with high efficiency (Franze et al. 2007). The vertebrate retina is now known to be a very efficient, highly sophisticated design. We have also discovered the reason why the photoreceptors need to be behind the layers of neural cells: The photoreceptors need an abundant blood supply, in close contact with them, to provide nutrients. If the capillary network were in front of the photoreceptors instead of immediately behind them, the relatively opaque blood cells would cause more problems than the neural cells.

## Evidence for Limits to Evolutionary Change

If modern life forms evolved from simple beginnings to their present state, then evolution must have essentially unlimited ability to produce new genes, new structures, and new body types. Does the evidence support this concept of unlimited evolution? Is there a biochemical process capable of this? Or is there a limit to the types of changes evolution can produce, and can we see evidence of such a limit?

### *Irreducible Complexity*

A group of scientists and philosophers who are members of the Intelligent Design (ID) Movement argue that life can only be explained by design. Michael Behe and other advocates of ID do not concern themselves with the nature or identity of a particular designer, but they evaluate evidence which seems to require that life resulted from some type of intelligent design. Behe elaborated these ideas in a book titled *Darwin's Black Box* (1996). In the era of Charles Darwin knowledge of the intricacies of molecular biology was far in the future. To biologists of the 19th century, the cell was a black box—they had almost no knowledge of what was going on within it. Darwin stated that if any biological structure could be found that could not evolve one small step at a time, his theory would absolutely break down (Darwin 1859). Behe contends that recent advances in molecular biology have met Darwin's challenge and broken down a crucial part of Darwin's theory: There are structures in living things that could not evolve one small step at a time, because they consist of several complex parts that must all be present at once or the structure will not work. Behe calls these structures irreducibly complex; they have to exist in a complex state or they do not function, and thus could not form by mutation and natural selection, one step at a time.

One example that Behe discusses is the bacterial flagellum. It is a long tail-like structure that rotates rapidly and acts like an outboard motor to propel bacteria through a fluid. The tail consists of numerous, complex proteins, each of which exhibits highly specific, fine structure; and it is driven by a proton motor that is amazingly like an electric motor in structure and function. While there is considerable variation in the structural details of flagella in different bacteria, all contain several of these basic parts, and it appears that removal of any of the critical parts eliminates flagellar function. Bacteria have other structures with a different function (like a syringe, secreting chemical substances) but with a number of the same essential parts as a flagellum, and critics of ID sometimes suggest that these structures may have been co-opted in the evolution of flagella. However, these structures also must have all the complex critical parts in order to function. Furthermore, phylogenetic analysis suggests that the flagellum appeared before its presumed precursor!

Behe's critics claim to have destroyed his theory of irreducible complexity by emphasizing the variations in structure of flagella and the secretory structures. However, Behe is raising a valid issue, and his critics will be more convincing if they directly address his central questions. Their response focuses more on a philosophical rejection of design rather than on convincing scientific answers to the questions ID raises. In reality, this debate between ID advocates and critics is not likely to find a definitive scientific resolution. Proponents of ID raise legitimate, important challenges, and so far their critics have not addressed these challenges (Behe 1996; Brand 2008).

Behe has written another book, *The Edge of Evolution* (2007), which takes a different approach to defining the limits of what evolution can do. Behe accepts the theory of descent of all life from a common ancestor (although he provides little evidence to support that theory), but he explores evidence of the degree of change in organisms with very short generation times, such as bacteria and the single-celled parasite that causes malaria. Even these organisms that have population sizes in the trillions and short reproduction times have not been able to evolve any significant new features. New developments, such as resistance to toxins, have resulted from loss, rather than gain, of genetic information (Spetner 1998). Behe concludes that mutation and natural selection seem to have a very limited ability to make biochemical changes.

### *The Evolution of New Genes by Duplication and Selection*

There is a theory of how new biological information evolves, in the form of new genes, and we will now consider whether this theory has adequate supporting evidence. As noted in chapter 2, some families of proteins, such as the hemoglobins, are a little different from each other but have the same basic function. Some of these could presumably arise by microevolutionary changes from the original hemoglobin.

However, the origin of a new gene with a novel function requires a different explanation, and this is where the theory of gene duplication comes into play. The first step in this process consists of an error in the DNA-copying process that makes an extra copy of a gene. The original gene continues to carry out its normal function, and consequently the copy has no necessary function and is free to mutate without restriction. In time the series of mutations could, theoretically, change it into a new gene, coding for a new protein with a novel function (Fig 3). All new proteins that are not just microevolutionary variants would need to originate by a process

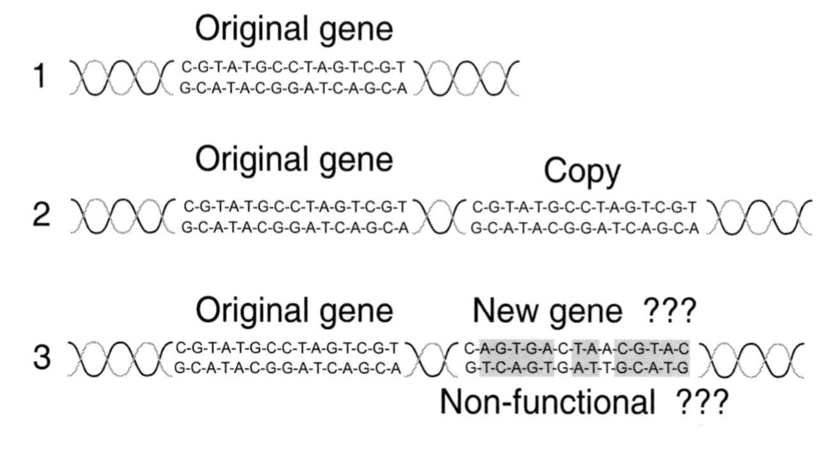


**Figure 3**—The theory of genetic evolution by gene duplication. A mutation makes a copy of a gene, and then the copy begins to mutate.

like this. If all life resulted from evolution, this process would have to happen many times, making new gene complexes, new proteins, and new combinations of proteins, joined in intricate ways as novel physiological systems that did not exist before.

There is one, absolutely critical, central step in the theory of gene duplication, and this is key to the entire theory of megaevolution. If this step does not work, then the theory of the origin of new body plans by megaevolution collapses. Genes that define the amino-acid sequence in proteins contain thousands of nucleotides. These do not all have to be precisely defined for the protein to work, but a significant number of them do have to be just right. The others can vary within limits. As a duplicate gene begins to mutate, with point mutations each changing a nucleotide, natural selection will need to preserve the needed mutations so the new protein will reach a new functional sequence. But the mutation process does not know what will be needed to make the new protein. Mutations are random in relation to what the organism needs. It depends on natural selection to select the helpful mutations and eliminate the rest. Figure 4 illustrates a problem in this process.

To make a new protein, natural selection will need to preserve the helpful mutations and eliminate the damaging ones (Fig. 4A). The problem is that there may be many steps in the process before the new protein acquires any new function. Before that time, selection cannot operate, because natural selection, like mutation, has no ability to know what will be needed in the future. It can only select among variants available at a moment in time, and cannot foresee what would be helpful later (Meyer 2013). Until the gene is producing a new protein with at least a minimal level of the new function, the mutation process will wander randomly, and natural selection is powerless to do anything about that (Fig. 4B).

In Figure 4B some mutations are going in the direction needed to make the new protein. At the same time, other mutations are going in the wrong direction. One nucleotide may mutate in the needed direction, but there is a high probability that it will later mutate away from that condition. Is there a process that can and will recognize the needed mutations and protect them from elimination by additional mutations until the entire suite of necessary changes is in place to produce a new protein ready to begin a new function? The answer seems to be no. The new gene and its protein will mutate randomly unless and until, purely by chance, it acquires its new function. Natural selection can only come into play after the gene has acquired the new function. If that happens, selection may then be involved in refining its effectiveness.

Another way to express this is that evolution cannot produce anything new *unless the needed mutations are available at the time they are needed.* Unless this is true, natural selection is powerless to do anything. And this is just the beginning. A new protein would be quite useless until it has a set of regulatory genes to control when, where, and in what quantities the protein will be produced. And this implies that selection could

```
A                       B
protein number one      protein number one
pjotein numper one      prjtein nuhber one
pjotain numper ene      prjtegn nuhber onc
tjofain numper ene      pvjtegn nuhbep onc
tjo ain nubper ene      prjtegn nuhbepuonc
tho ain nhbper ene      pkjtegn nuhbepuoic
tho adn nhbprr ene      pkjtesn nuhpepuoic
tho adnxnhbprr eie      bkjtesn nuhpepdoic
the adfxnhbprr eie      bkjtxsn nuopepdoic
the tdfxnhbprrueie      bkjtxsn nuohevdoic
the tdjxnhbprrteie      bkjtfsn nuohnvdoic
the tdjgnhcprrteie      tkjtfsn tuohnvdoic
the tajgnycprrteie      tkjtfsd tgohnvdoic
the tajgntzprrteie      tkjtfsd tgehnvdojc
the targntjprrteie      tkjtfsdktgehnvdsjc
the targnt prrteig      tkjrfsdktgeh vdsjc
__________________      __________________
the targnt prrtein      the targnt prrtein
the targnt protein      the targnt protein
the target protein      the target protein
```

**Figure 4**—Two series of mutations, using letters to symbolize amino acids in a protein, with a meaningful phrase representing a functional protein. There are two mutations in each step. In example A, a series of mutations converts one gene into a new gene producing a protein with a different function, if natural selection is recognizing and preserving positive mutations at each step. Example B is a series of truly random mutations. Some mutations are constructive changes toward the new gene, but unless the new gene is already functional and selected for, those constructive changes are just as likely to change again, away from the target. Evolution of a new gene and protein would involve many more mutations, but the principle would be the same: Example B is a far more probable series of events. In this example, each step below the horizontal line is functional to some extent, with the last one fully functional.

probably not even recognize a new potentially functional protein, even if it did accidently evolve, until those regulatory genes had also evolved through chance mutations.

Many changes in organisms are not caused by new structural (protein-coding) genes, but by changes in regulatory genes that control the location, timing, and amount of protein synthesis of individual proteins. Existing regulatory genes can vary by normal microevolutionary processes of mutation and natural selection, resulting in new adaptations. But if new structures or new physiological processes are to evolve, there will need to be new regulatory genes to control these processes. The evolution of these new genes will encounter the same problems summarized above with regard to the coding genes. The needed mutations *must be available when needed,* and until the new gene has become minimally functional, *natural selection cannot assist* the process. And even if a new gene does happen to form, the new gene cannot become functional until it becomes integrated with the other genes in a functional gene complex, an intertwined set of coding genes and their regulatory genes.

Until an answer can be found to this considerable dilemma, the theory of megaevolution rests on a very shaky foundation. In reality it rests on faith, just as the theory of Creation rests on faith (Brand 2009; Meyer 2013; Shapiro 2011). The difference between these two concepts of origins is that an intelligent Creator would know how to design and put together the whole complex of coding genes and their regulatory genes to form a functional whole. In contrast, natural selection has no power to understand ahead of time what will be needed to accomplish that. This is an added level of irreducible complexity that will challenge the theory of megaevolution by mutation and natural selection. We have abundant evidence of how intelligent beings can design and invent complex things, and we do not normally see that happening as the result of unintelligent processes.

It has often been stated that if microevolution occurs, it will lead inevitably to megaevolution of everything. The issues we have just discussed pose a major challenge to that claim. Unless there is a way to assure that the specific needed mutations will be available *when needed,* and unless these changes *are selected for* at essentially each step, there is a biochemical "Grand Canyon" between microevolution and megaevolution (Fig. 5). Evolution will only happen within each created body plan, using the genetic potential given it by design.

## The Options for Explaining Life and Their Implications

For many of us, it seems incomprehensible that an unintelligent process could evolve the amazing wonders of life. But we wish for more than amazement. If evolution is not enough to produce life, we would like to be able to understand the biochemical reason why it is not enough. I suggest that the discussion above focuses on the core of the reason why evolution is not able to produce the living world. Critics of creationism would likely reply that we are just not being creative enough to understand the evolutionary process. Given the worldview they are working in, that is a reasonable approach, but they are only expressing their faith in the theory of megaevolution. They say we should not reject the accepted theory of evolution of life just because we do not have all the answers. We never know what will be discovered

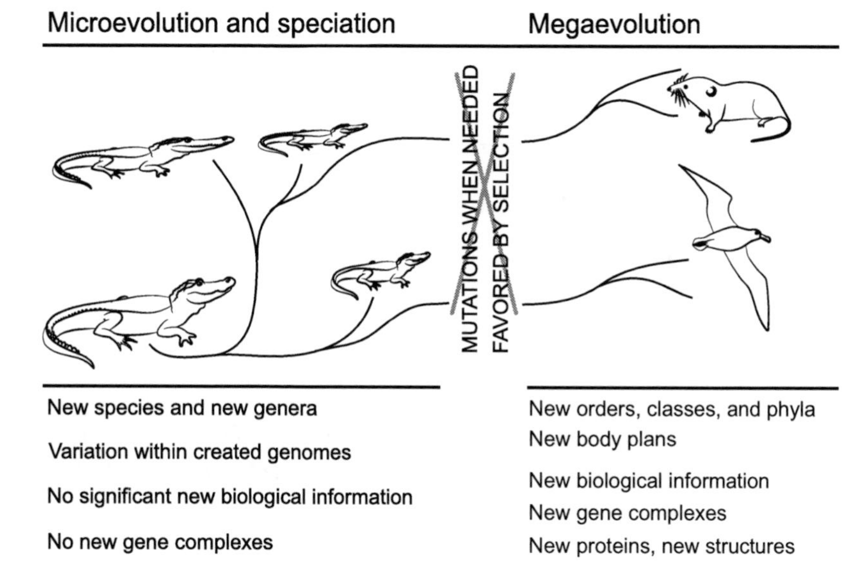


**Figure 5**—Left: a phylogenetic tree with several species of reptiles produced by microevolution and speciation. Right: presumed continuation of that phylogenetic tree to produce mammals and birds from the reptile ancestors by megaevolution. Middle: two conditions, not supported by evidence, but necessary for megaevolution to produce new biological information and new gene complexes. The X represents the biochemical Grand Canyon separating megaevolution from microevolution—the reason it is very doubtful that megaevolution could ever work.

in the future. Those who use that reasoning are expressing their complete confidence in their theory and their commitment to following that theory to its final conclusion.

There is something to be said for that logic. After all, those of us who accept a biblical view of a recent Creation have to use similar logic. We also have unanswered questions, and we have to wait for future research to provide answers. Two of the biggest questions arise from the radiometric time scale and the sequence of fossils in the geological column that looks like an evolutionary sequence of at least the vertebrates (please refer to the discussion in chapter 5). But we also have reason to have faith in our Bible-based worldview. Given the unanswered questions that face both models—origin of all life by megaevolution and biblical Creation—how might we proceed? Let us consider three possibilities.

The first approach is to accept the conventional naturalistic understanding of the origin of all organisms by megaevolution, and to assume some answers will be found to explain how life originated and how to solve the seeming biochemical dead end for evolving fundamentally new biological information. Of course, for those who accept this explanation, the Genesis story of Creation is false; humans evolved from other primates; there was no literal, sinless Adam and Eve at the beginning of life on earth; and the Bible is not the authoritative source of God's revelation.

On the other hand, we can take the second option: to have confidence in the literal biblical story of a recent six-day Creation, followed by adaptations through evolution at the level of microevolution, speciation, and the origin of (on average) perhaps genera and some families. Adam and Eve were the first humans, they fell into sin in the Garden, and the story of redemption that provides the solution to the problem of sin and evil. This is the Great Controversy between Christ and Satan, the only satisfactory explanation of the problem of evil, pain, and suffering, and its final solution is to come. Accepting this worldview brings a coherent Bible-based, Christ-centered theology and hope for eternal life. Along with this come some unanswered questions about how to explain major geological phenomena such as the radiometric time scale and the sequence of fossils. I have pondered these questions frequently, but I am confident that the God who inspired the Bible writers knows infinitely more about geology than any of us, and I put my trust in Him, not in any human understanding of things that happened long ago, before any modern scientists were here to observe them.

Near the beginning of this chapter I said we would also consider a third possible explanation: theistic evolution, which combines the first two options and which is becoming common in the broader scholarly Christian community. This worldview essentially accepts the entire secular theory of evolution and geological history, and attempts to combine that with Christian faith. God is believed to have been, in some way, involved with the evolutionary process through the ages, but not in a way that could be detected by science. In theistic evolution all life is the result of evolution: humans evolved from primates, and life began through some type of spontaneous origin, but this was all part of God's method of creation (Brand 2006b; Brand and Davidson 2013).

It appears that theistic evolutionists generally hold their position because contemporary science has convinced them that all life resulted from evolution through millions of years. If that conclusion is combined with belief in God, the result is some type of theistic evolution. But before accepting theistic evolution, it seems wise to consider the implications of that choice. If God used evolution to produce life, that means that all the evil, pain, disease, death, and suffering involved in millions of years of evolution are also part of God's plan. There was no literal Adam and Eve who fell into sin before the existence of evil, suffering, and death, as described in Genesis. Theistic evolution has no room for the Great Controversy between Christ and Satan. All approaches to theistic evolution (or evolutionary creation, and its cousin, progressive creation) greatly diminish God in some way. For if the theory were true, then much of Genesis is false, and what reason would we have for confidence in the rest of the Bible? Jesus and the New Testament writers accepted the reality of the Genesis creation, and God wrote the 4th commandment with His own finger, but why did they believe in a literal Creation if it is false and theistic evolution is true? In addition, the concepts presented earlier in this chapter and others beyond the scope of this brief essay (e.g., Walton 2012; Brand 2009; Meyer 2013) raise doubts about the validity of megaevolution and deep time. These are reasons why I cannot accept megaevolution, whether it be atheistic or theistic.

## Conclusion

How do we know how God has guided the design process of His Creation? How can we decide the role of the miraculous in the history of life on earth, and can we define it within the limits of evolution? A little history will help to answer this question. This is the history of my own thinking, but I know there are others who shared a similar process. I used to think that very little evolutionary change has occurred. While I never believed in fixity of species, I was doubtful that very much change was possible in the brief time since Creation. But in the last two or three decades new findings in genetics and development have opened the door to the possibility of more rapid and larger-scale change, especially when nested in the framework of a created genetic system with created gene pools for each body type. Thus, instead of very limited evolution, perhaps within a genus, it now seems like these created systems would allow change up to the family level, and in some cases maybe a little higher (as with parasites). Such evolution is possible because of the genetic system that existed in the beginning, with the built-in potential for adaptation. It does not depend on the unlikely possibility of the right random mutations being available when needed. The limits of how much change can be produced by this system seem to be determined by the very nature of the genetic system.

There are only two ways to know how God does things: either He tells us, or our scientific research indicates how He works. Research since the Middle Ages has convinced most of us that God normally runs the universe through His laws of nature. Because we can count on the consistent operation of those laws on a daily basis, scientific research is possible.

The topic of origins is a little different. Knowing how things operate today does not tell us how they originated, and the laws of chemistry and physics do not indicate how life began. The Bible gives us the basic story of Creation, but it leaves most details unexplained. Certainly there must have been more than one option for how God could make the genetic and biochemical systems, how He could design groups of animals and plants, and how much subsequent change was to be provided for in their genetic composition. We have to study nature and the written Word to learn how God did these things—to understand the interface between His original designs and the changes that have occurred within the created groups. This is not the god-of-the-gaps theory, inventing miracles to explain things we do not understand. It is the opposite. The more we learn about nature, and the better we understand it, the more we can say about how God operated in originating the life forms on earth. But we can only reach trustworthy conclusions if the Word of God is our guide, steering us in the right direction as nature fills in certain details.

The theory that all of life descended from a common ancestor is consistent with part of the evidence in the fossil record, but this is not adequate to demonstrate the truth of the theory. The fossil record indicates the sequence in which the fossils were buried, but so far we do not have the evidence to tell us why they are in this sequence.

Charles Darwin, along with most modern biologists, came to the belief that all life forms arose through megaevolution by mutation and natural selection. In Darwin's time megaevolution was strictly a hypothesis that was accepted because of a commitment to a noncreationist worldview, based on the assumption of naturalism. Modern biology research tools have vastly more potential to test that hypothesis than Darwin could ever have dreamed of. But genetic and biochemical evidence to support the hypothesis of megaevolution—the evolution of major groups of life forms by mutation and natural selection—remains unconvincing. The modern commitment of most of the scientific community to common descent by megaevolution is still based on faith in a naturalistic worldview, not on confirmation by biochemical evidence (Meyer 2013; Shapiro 2011; Brand 2009).

Both worldviews reach conclusions that are faith based. Faith is based on evidence, but not proof. We all must make choices for which we lack absolute proof. Do we know Jesus? Do we know Him and the Bible well enough to make this choice with confidence?

We began this discussion with a conversation among Darwin, Wallace, and Blyth. I have to conclude, based on both Scripture and science, that Blyth and Wallace were closer to the truth than Darwin and that Darwin himself made a very big mistake. Yes, there is a process of evolutionary change, but it is change within definite limits. The limits are the boundaries of the created genetic system and the created gene pools of the original body plans. Evolution can bring out previously unused genetic potential, resulting in new species and adaptations to changing environments, but it has almost no ability to create new biological information and it cannot produce a new body plan. Those body plans came from the creative genius of God, expressed in the genomes of the creatures and the plants He created in the beginning as described in the book Genesis.

## Literature Cited

Ayala, F. J. 2006. Darwin and Intelligent Design. Fortress Press, Minneapolis.
Behe, M. J. 1996. Darwin's black box: The biochemical challenge to evolution. The Free Press, New York.
Behe, M. J. 2007. The edge of evolution: The search for the limits of Darwinism. Free Press, New York.
Bowler, P. J. 1990. Charles Darwin: The man and his influence. Cambridge University Press, New York.
Brand, L. 2006a. Beginnings: Are science and scripture partners in the search for origins? Pacific Press, Nampa, Idaho.
Brand, L. 2006b. A biblical perspective on the philosophy of science. Origins 59:6–42.
Brand, L. 2008. A critique of current anti-ID arguments and ID responses. Origins 63:5–23.
Brand, L. 2009. Faith, reason and earth history. 2nd ed. Andrews University Press, Berrien Springs, Michigan.
Brand, L. R. and R. M. Davidson. 2013. Choose you this day: Why it matters what you believe about creation. Pacific Press, Nampa, Idaho.
Coyne, J. A. 2009. Why evolution is true. Viking, New York.
Darwin, C. R. 1859. On the origin of species. John Murray, London.
Dawkins, R. 1986. The blind watchmaker. W.W. Norton & Co., New York.
Dawkins, R. 1996. Climbing mount improbable. W. W. Norton & Co., New York.
Eiseley, L. C. 1955. Was Darwin wrong about the human brain? Harper's 211(1266):66–70.
Eiseley, L. C. 1979. Darwin and the mysterious Mr. X. Harcourt Brace Jovanovich, New York.
Franze, K. et al. 2007. Müller cells are living optical fibers in the vertebrate retina. Proceedings of the National Academy of Sciences 104:8287–8292.
Gould, S. J. 1980. The panda's thumb: More reflections in natural history. W.W. Norton & Co., New York.
Gould, S. J. 1994. Common pathways of illumination. Natural History 103(12):10–20.
Landgren, P. 1993. On the origin of "species" ideological roots of the species concept. Pp. 47–64 in Typen des Lebens (S. Sherer, ed.). Pascal-Verlag (Studium Integrale), Berlin.

Lester, L. P., and R. G. Bohlin. 1989. The natural limits to biological change, 2nd ed. Probe Books, Dallas, Texas.

Meyer, S. C. 2009. Signature in the cell. HarperOne, New York.

Meyer, S. C. 2013. Darwin's doubt. HaperOne, New York.

Meyer, S. C., S. Minnich, J. Moneymaker, P. A. Nelsen, and R. Seelke. 2007. Explore evolution: The arguments for and against Neo-Darwinism. Hill House, London.

Pearcey, N. 2005. Total truth: Liberating Christianity from its cultural captivity. Crossway Books, Wheaton, Illinois.

Roth, A. Origins: 1998. Linking science and scripture. Review and Herald Publishing Association, Silver Spring, Maryland.

Shapiro, J. A. 2011. Evolution: A view from the 21st century. FT Science Press, Upper Saddle Press, New Jersey.

Simpson, G. G. 1944. Tempo and mode in evolution. Columbia University Press, New York.

Spetner, L. 1998. Not by chance! Shattering the modern theory of evolution. The Judaica Press, Brooklyn, New York.

Thaxton, C. B., W. L. Bradley, and R. L. Olsen. 1984. The mystery of life's origin: Reassessing current theories. Philosophical Library, New York.

Walton, J. C. 2012. The natural limits of Neo-Darwinian evolution. Pp. 184–201 in Ball, B. W. In the beginning. Pacific Press, Nampa, Idaho.

Wiedershiem, R. 1895. The structure of man: An index to his past history. McMillan and Co., London.

Young, M., and T. Edis (eds.). 2004. Why intelligent design fails: A scientific critique of the new creationism. Rutgers University Press, New Brunswick, New Jersey.

## Chapter Five

# THE FOSSIL RECORD: SEVENTH-DAY ADVENTIST PERSPECTIVES


## H. Thomas Goodwin


Several years ago, students and I excavated Big John, the partial skeleton of an American mastodon discovered in southwestern Michigan. The bones were buried in organic-rich sediments along with fossil wood (a few pieces had been chewed by an ancient beaver), spruce cones, and the tooth of a muskrat. Fossil wood immediately beneath one of the bones yielded a carbon-14 age estimate of just over 12,200 C-14 years before present, indicating that this animal lived and died near the end of the Ice Age (Pleistocene).

The discovery and excavation of this mastodon was exciting but not unique. Paleontologists have reported over 200 American mastodon and nearly 50 Jefferson's mammoth finds from southern Michigan (Fig. 1A). American mastodons represented an extinct family of elephant-like creatures whereas mammoths were true elephants, but both were members of the mammal order Proboscidea. These giants, along with a variety of other now-extinct species, such as giant beaver and woodland muskox, occupied southern Michigan during the late stages of the Ice Age, as ice melted back from the region (Holman 2001:75). Clearly, Michigan was once a very different place!

Finds such as these raise intriguing questions for Adventist biologists. How do these ancient creatures fit into God's creation? What do they tell us about the history of life and of the earth? How does that history relate to what we learn from a study of the Bible, especially the accounts of Creation and the Flood given in Genesis? Seventh-day Adventist scholars have been fascinated by these questions for over 100 years and, as we shall see, have offered a variety of potential answers.

The present chapter describes approaches by some Seventh-day Adventists to the fossil record and its interpretation. First, we will consider what fossils indicate about the diversity of life in the past and explore questions Adventist writers have raised about the origins of some ancient creatures. Second, we will summarize what science has learned about the sequence of life forms in the fossil record and how evolutionary interpretations of that sequence offer a challenge to Adventist thought. Third, the chapter will survey the subsequent responses of Adventist scholars who have critiqued conventional interpretations, developed alternative theories, and done original research—all framed by a commitment to be faithful to biblical revelation. Finally, the chapter will suggest future possibilities for Adventist study of the fossil record.

Let me emphasize: this chapter only samples the rich literature written by Seventh-day Adventist scholars about the fossil record! I have focused on a few themes and used representative examples to illustrate each one.

**Figure 1**—Extinct members of the mammal order Proboscidea that illustrate variability within this group. A) *Mammuthus jeffersoni* from the Pleistocene of southwestern Michigan and displayed in the Andrews University Natural History Museum. B) Lower jaw of *Amebelodon,* one of the shovel-tuskers from the Miocene of North America. Displayed in the Texas Memorial Museum, Austin, Texas. C) Lower jaw of *Deinotherium* from Germany. Displayed in the University of Nebraska Museum of Natural History, Lincoln, Nebraska. Note also the shovel-tusker partially displayed in the background. All photos taken by the author.

Furthermore, I have not attempted to survey the broad literature on geology, unless directly relevant to the themes developed in this chapter. Several Adventist authors have written book-length treatments on evolution, paleontology, and geology (e.g., Brand 2009; Coffin et al. 2005; Roth 1998), which I encourage you to consult.

## Fossils, Life's Diversity, and God's Creation

Fossils reveal the spectacular diversity and variety of life forms that no longer live on Earth. To illustrate, we will consider the mammal order Proboscidea, which includes only three species of modern elephants but over 150 extinct species in the fossil record (Gheerbrant et al. 2005). Mastodons and mammoths were both proboscideans, and so were the so-called shovel-tuskers, bizarre creatures that sported forward-pointing, flattened lower tusks that looked much like flat-tipped shovels (Fig. 1B). Deinotheres likewise displayed lower tusks, but their tusks projected downward (Fig. 1C), not forward (Prothero and Schoch 2002). Numerous other fossil taxa are assigned to this order, but we will note just one more: *Phosphatherium.* This curious animal had some proboscidean features (for example, teeth with broad cross-ridges) but was very small—about the size of a fox (Gheerbrant et al. 2005).

How do ancient creatures such as these fit into God's creation? Seventh-day Adventists have been intrigued by this question, but most attention has been focused on a debate about the origin of one particular group—the dinosaurs (reviewed by Hayward 1993b). This diverse and varied group comprises over 500 known genera that differ greatly in size, anatomy, and mode of life (Wang and Dodson 2006). One view builds on two comments in Ellen White's writings. First, she refers to "a class of

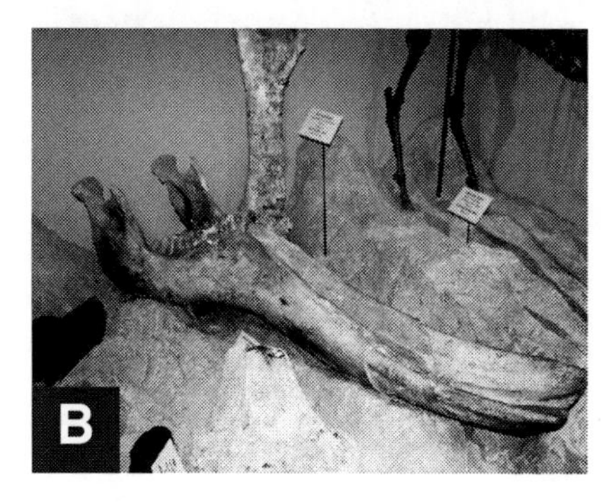


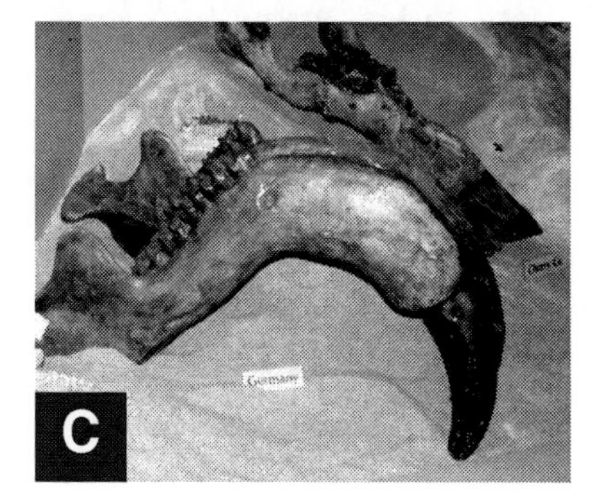

very large animals which perished at the flood" (White 1864b:121). White did not identify these "very large" animals, but a number of Adventists have interpreted her remarks as referring to dinosaurs. Second, she wrote, "The confused species which God did not create, which were the result of amalgamation, were destroyed by the flood" (White 1864:75). In this view, antediluvian man or Satan "created" dinosaurs through genetic manipulation (amalgamation in 19th-century language), and the various dinosaurs subsequently perished because God did not preserve them on the ark. David Read, an attorney with an avid interest in dinosaurs, has presented a book-length argument for the theory (2009). Cross-breeding between classes has also been suggested for the origin of odd transitional fossils such as the reptile-like bird *Archaeopteryx* (Clark 1940).

The second view in this debate argues that dinosaurs were part of God's creation just as large animals of today represent the Creator's handiwork (Hayward 1993a).

However one comes down on this debate, the genetic manipulation view has not been suggested as a general explanation for the marvelous variety and rich diversity preserved as fossils. Fossils document nearly 4,400 families of extinct organisms that include a wide range of exotic plants, mammals (how about a group of rodents with horns?), marine and flying reptiles, giant amphibians, armored fish, and a plethora of marine invertebrates and microorganisms (Benton 1993). One extinct group alone, the marine trilobites, varied widely in size and body form (note dramatic differences depicted in Fig. 2), with paleontologists recognizing roughly 160 families (Benton 1993) and 4,000 valid genera from the fossil record (estimated from data in Jell and Adrain 2002). This rich tapestry of life seems to testify to God's creativity, although most Adventists recognize that much change has occurred since creation. Leonard Brand, for example, argues that originally created species may have had genetic systems and gene pools that allowed rapid and significant change, perhaps to the level of families or even higher in some cases (see chapter 4).

## The Fossil Sequence: Conventional Interpretations

Paleontologists find most fossils in sedimentary strata: layers of ancient mud, sand, gravel, and so on that usually have turned to rock. In the early

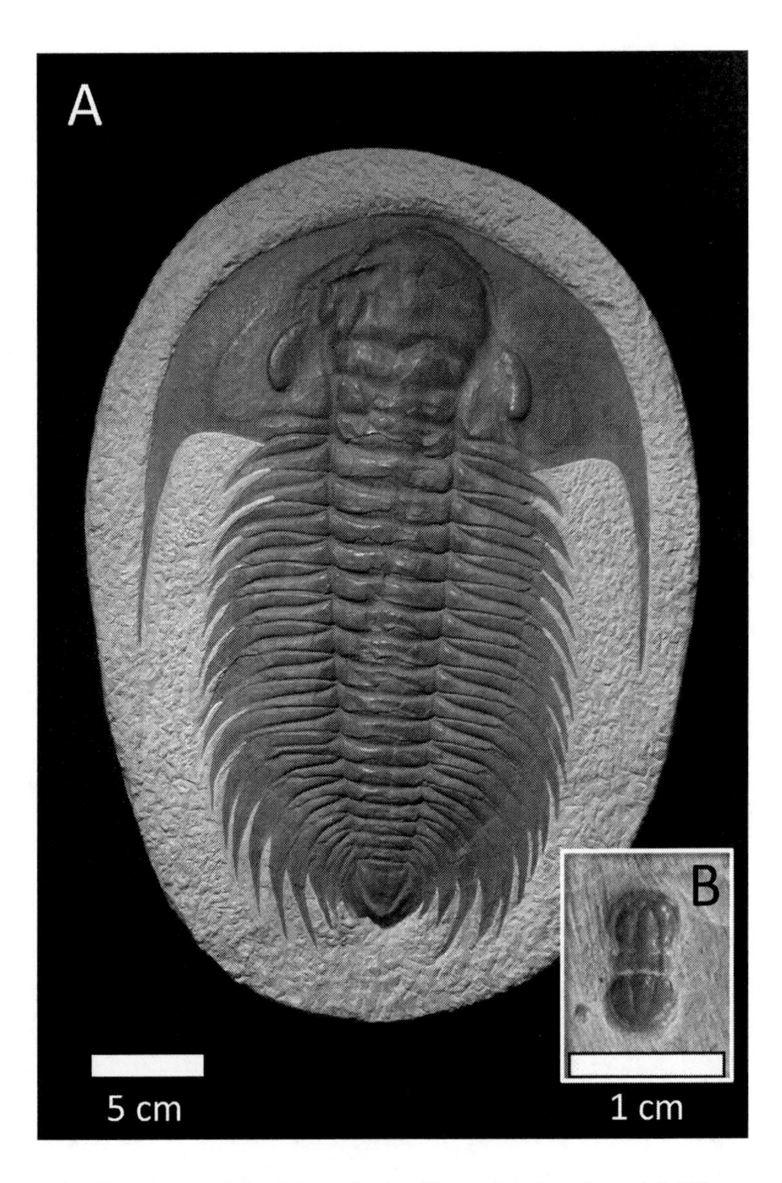


**Figure 2**—Two genera of Cambrian trilobites illustrating the substantial differences in size and body form that occur within this group. A) *Acadoparadoxides* from Morocco, Africa. Cast obtained from PaleoScene (www.paleo.cc). B) *Peronopsis* from Utah. Both specimens are part of the paleontology teaching collection, Department of Biology, Andrews University, and photographed by the author. Note significant difference in scale between A) and B).

1800s, William Smith and others noticed an important pattern: fossil-bearing strata occurred in a particular stratigraphic sequence that could be observed repeatedly and at different locations, with each stratum containing a somewhat distinctive assemblage of fossils. Geologists soon realized that the sequence of strata at any given location was incomplete, but, with careful fieldwork, and taking advantage of distinctive fossils characterizing particular strata, they were able to work out a more complete sequence. This work culminated in production of the geologic column, a stratigraphic map that shows how various strata relate to each other in a comprehensive, vertical sequence (Fig. 3). The lowest strata (with their fossils) were obviously laid down before strata and fossils that lie above them.

Let us illustrate the fossil sequence, using groups introduced in the preceding section. Paleozoic strata commonly yield trilobites, sometimes in astonishing diversity, but they never yield dinosaurs or proboscideans. In contrast, Mesozoic strata entirely lack trilobites, but appropriate deposits commonly contain dinosaurs. Finally, Cenozoic strata never yield trilobites or dinosaurs, but suitable terrestrial deposits often contain fossil proboscideans—especially strata assigned to the upper Cenozoic (Miocene-Pleistocene).

The sequence of fossils holds not only at the broad scale of geological eras (Paleozoic, Mesozoic, Cenozoic), but also at much finer scales, especially at the local level. Let us return to proboscideans to illustrate. The fox-sized proboscidean, *Phosphatherium,* is known only from the lower Eocene strata of North Africa, followed by other African species in the Eocene and Oligocene (Gheerbrant et al. 2005). In contrast, the diverse shovel-tuskers were restricted to Miocene deposits of North America (Lambert and Shoshani 1998). Mastodons first appeared in Miocene strata and persisted to the end of the Pleistocene, but mammoths do not show up until the Pliocene—and do not appear in the North American record until the Pleistocene (Lister and Bahn 2007).

Although most of those who worked out the fossil sequence were Christians, many of these men concluded that the earth had experienced a long history, much longer than the 6,000 years traditionally inferred from the Bible. They sought harmony between the Bible and long ages in various ways, but a common attempt was to view the days of Genesis as indefinite periods of time during which God sequentially created advancing life forms (Ramm 1954), a view now referred to as progressive creation.

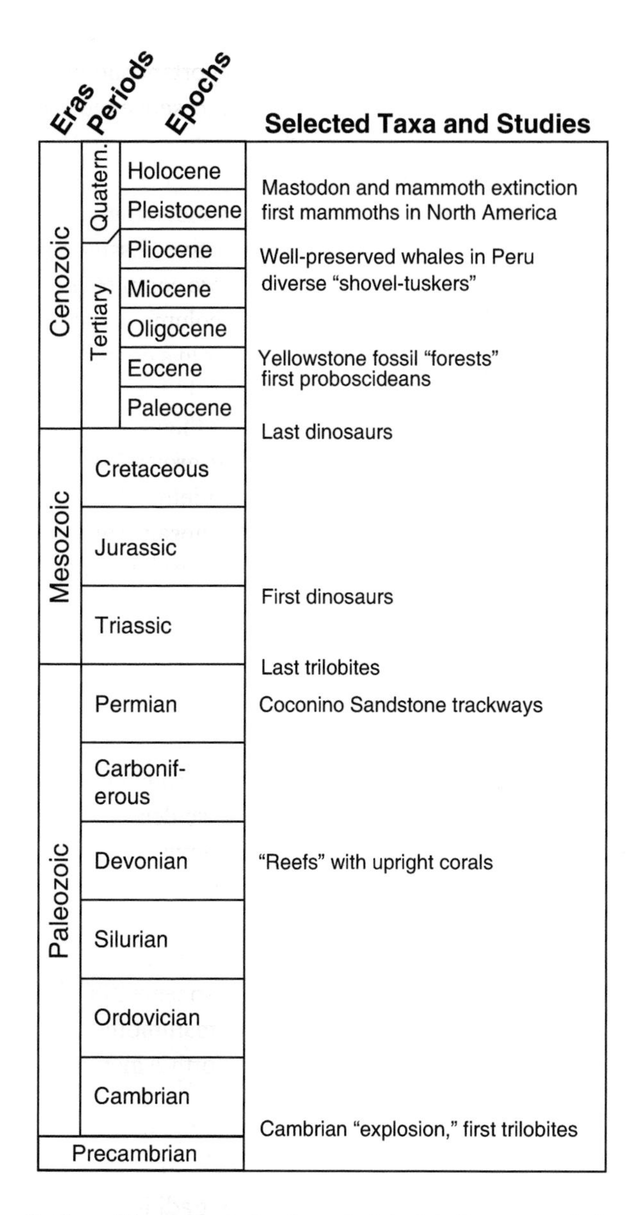


**Figure 3**—Outline of the geological column that depicts the eras, periods, and epochs for the fossil-rich portion of the record. Details of Precambrian stratigraphy are not shown. Stratigraphically lowest and highest records of several groups mentioned in the text are given, as well as several fossil sites studied by Seventh-day Adventist scientists and mentioned in the text (in italics).

Since the discovery of the fossil sequence, conventional geology has retained belief in the antiquity of life on earth, but it was not until the mid-1900s that scientists developed well-accepted, quantitative methods for estimating age. These methods use the regular, clock-like decay of radioactive isotopes in rock or bone to infer the age of geological samples, and the ages they arrive at are very old.[1] For example, geologists now interpret the base of the Cambrian (stratigraphically lowest trilobites) to be roughly 540 million years old, the top of the Cretaceous (stratigraphically highest dinosaurs) to be about 65 million years old, and the end of the Pleistocene (last mastodons and mammoths in Michigan) to have occurred about 11,000 years ago. We will consider how Adventist scientists have responded to these interpretations later in this essay.

With the development of evolutionary theory in the mid-1800s, Darwin and others proposed a new explanation for the fossil sequence: that the sequence of life forms recorded, however imperfectly, the evolutionary history of life over vast periods of time. Early evolutionists knew that the fossil record did not perfectly fit the theory—Darwin was perplexed, for example, by the sudden appearance of many animal groups (including trilobites) at the base of the Paleozoic without evidence of ancestors—but they attributed these challenges to imperfections of the geological record. Paleontology has progressed significantly since the time of Darwin, but good intermediate fossils between major groups remain few in number (e.g., Carroll 1997:3–4).

Despite such challenges, most paleontologists now accept an evolutionary explanation for life's history, and they point to a number of fossils with transitional attributes and intermediate stratigraphic placement as evidence for this conclusion. Examples include fossils that are in some respects transitional between fish and four-footed land animals (recently complicated by well-preserved trackways indicating that four-footed animals were present stratigraphically lower than the transitional fossils [Niedzwiedzki et al. 2010]), reptiles and birds, an extinct group of fossil vertebrates and mammals, tiny early horses and modern horses,

1. Many of the methods are somewhat complex and beyond the scope of this chapter. The interested reader can find a good introductory description of these methods in any historical geology text. Brand (2009) provides an accessible, basic introduction.

land mammals and whales, and so on (summarized in Prothero 2007).[2] To return to an example we have explored in this chapter, the stratigraphically lowest proboscidean yet known, *Phosphatherium,* has some but not all features now diagnostic of this order (e.g., it has teeth with broad cross-ridges like proboscideans, but it is very small in size), consistent with it being in some respects transitional (although it remains poorly known). The subsequent record of proboscideans likewise can be interpreted as an evolutionary story: in this view, the group first evolved and diversified in Africa, and subsequently spread throughout Eurasia and the New World, with lineages evolving through time to fill various niches (Prothero and Schoch 2002).

The Christians who worked out the geologic column in the early 1800s were staunchly anti-evolutionist, at least initially. However, some Christians subsequently accepted evolution and adopted a view known as theistic evolution: God created life forms, but He did so using the natural processes of evolutionary change. This view has become a common perspective among some biologists (Collins 2006; Falk 2004).

Despite their popularity among Christian biologists, long-age models for the creation of life remain problematic for Adventists. First, a close analysis of the Genesis texts supports the conclusion that early Genesis is best interpreted as a straightforward, historical narrative (Davidson 2003; Hasel 1994). Second, several authors have sketched out theological challenges posed by progressive creation and theistic evolution (see various papers in Baldwin 2000; Brand, chapter 4 in this book). Of particular concern to Adventists, both progressive creation and theistic evolution indicate that the long history of life and death preserved in the fossil record preceded the appearance of humans (in the early Pleistocene), requiring that predation and death (at least animal death) occurred before human sin. Thus, these views raise difficult questions about God's character of love, and they appear to break the link between sin and death revealed in the book of Romans (Baldwin 1991).

To summarize, careful scientific work, especially in the early 1800s, established that fossil-bearing strata are preserved in a characteristic sequence. Initially, geologists interpreted this sequence to reflect God's work of progressive creation over long periods of time, but most abandoned

---

2. Prothero presents numerous examples of transitional fossils, but the reader should be aware that his survey exhibits an intensely anti-creationist bias.

that view with the advent of evolutionary explanations. While some Christians have accepted evolution as God's means of creating life, Adventists have maintained belief in a literal reading of Genesis. How then have Adventists addressed the fossil sequence and its interpretation? Let us now turn to that question.

## Seventh-day Adventist Interpretations

In the main, Seventh-day Adventist scholars have sought to harmonize Genesis and the fossil-bearing rock record through the theory of Flood geology. Flood geologists agree that 1) a few thousand years ago the earth was organized and the biosphere created in 6 literal days; 2) this harmonious creation was subsequently disrupted because of human sin; and 3) much of the fossil-bearing rock record was laid down rapidly (within about one year) during the great judgment event of the Old Testament brought on by humanity's wickedness—the Flood.

Flood geology shares much with so-called scriptural geology of the mid-1800s (Johns 2008), but the modern expression of the theory was born in the prolific writing of George McCready Price, a Seventh-day Adventist and self-taught geologist active in the early to mid-1900s. Price's work defined Adventist thought on the issue for the first half of the 1900s and subsequently came to shape how Christian fundamentalists relate the Bible and science (Numbers 2006). As we will see, Adventist creationists have moved well beyond Price's ideas since the mid-1900s.

Because of shared history (traced back to Price), Adventist Flood geologists often have much in common with the broader community of Christian fundamentalists. However, Adventists are unique in at least one way: Many accept the great antiquity of the cosmos, solar system, and even the rocks of the earth, arguing that the Genesis account concerns the shaping of materials for life and subsequent creation of the biosphere. This view has allowed some Adventists to accept great radiometric ages for earth's rocks, but not its fossils (e.g., Brown 1981). In contrast, most fundamentalists insist that the entire universe was created in the six days of Creation.

A significant and unresolved discussion amongst Flood geologists is, Where do Flood-deposited sediments begin and end in the rock record? A common view is that, while precise and universal boundaries may not be definable, most of the Paleozoic, Mesozoic, and perhaps early Cenozoic strata were deposited catastrophically during the Flood—within about one year (Nichol 1978:89). Thick sequences of Precambrian strata have been interpreted as very ancient, laid down when the earth was "without form and void" before the six days of creation. (Roth [1992] suggested that the microbial prokaryote fossils sometimes found in Precambrian rocks perhaps derived from microbes that subsequently penetrated these ancient strata.)

With this background, let us now consider how Adventists have addressed three challenges presented to Flood geology: the great age of life on earth as interpreted by conventional geology, the fossil sequence discovered by field work in the 1800s, and evolutionary interpretations of that sequence proposed by Darwin and others. Scientists at the Geoscience Research Institute (GRI), an institute of the General Conference of Seventh-day Adventists that studies these issues, have done much of this work, and they often have published their finds in the GRI-sponsored journal, *Origins.*

### *Age of Life on Earth*

Adventist scientists have responded to the challenge of old fossil-bearing rocks in three ways: by critiquing radiometric dating, reinterpreting other time indicators, and marshaling evidence for a shorter time in earth's history. Let us consider each in turn.

Robert Brown, a physicist who was director at GRI, has written extensively about radiometric dating. He (1981) accepted a very old universe, which he viewed as strongly supported by science and allowed by the Bible, but he raised questions about the way geologists infer the age of fossils from the age of rocks associated with them (1977). Brown showed particular interest in carbon-14 dating, the method used to date geologically young fossils (such as Big John mentioned in the introduction) from the upper Pleistocene and Holocene. The technical aspects of this work go beyond the scope of this chapter, but in summary he argued that old carbon-14 dates (up to about 50,000 years old) likely resulted from a strikingly richer biosphere (with much more nonradioactive carbon to dilute carbon-14) before the Flood compared to today (Brown 1979).

Brown (1990) proposed a simple model for correcting carbon-14 dates based on biblical chronology. When applied, for example, to carbon-dated wood found with Big John, this model yields an estimated age between 4,800 and 4,850 years before present (based on a C-14 age of 12,200 years before present, and the Flood estimated at 5,000 years before present). Brown also summarized carbon-14 evidence consistent with a short chronology for life. For example, he noted the presence of measurable carbon-14 in samples interpreted to be millions of year old—unexpected given the relatively short half-life of this isotope—as consistent with biblical chronology (Brown 1988). Paul Giem, an Adventist physician with strong interest in earth history, has likewise advanced this argument (2001) as part of a general critique of radiometric dating (1997:116–190).

Radiometric dating provides the great age estimates employed in conventional geology, but other features of the rock record likewise pose challenges to Flood geology. For example, geologists recognize numerous fossil reefs in different strata. Reefs take time to form—years to millennia, depending on the size of the reef—thus their reported presence through the geologic record challenges Flood geology, which ascribes most of this record to catastrophic deposition in one year. In response to this challenge, Ariel Roth (1995), long-term director of GRI and active flood geologist, examined the literature on fossil reefs and proposed that many of them are not true reefs as we know them today (and thus may not be as great a challenge as was thought), whereas others may have grown before the Flood and been buried by that event. We will return to fossil reefs in a subsequent section of this chapter.

Finally, Adventist scientists have responded to great ages of conventional geology by tabulating features that seem to imply less time in the rock record. Roth (1986) has again spearheaded this effort, arguing that present rates of erosion, sediment transport to the oceans, mountain uplift, and volcanism (among other things) are much higher than rates inferred from the geologic record when it is interpreted as forming over conventional geologic time scales. He also discussed significant time gaps in the geological record—a relatively "young" deposit lies directly on a much "older" deposit, with the intervening time missing. According to Roth (1988), these time gaps often show little evidence for the weathering and erosion expected to occur over millions of years.

### *Fossil Sequence*

Adventist Flood geologists have taken two approaches to the fossil sequence. The first approach, championed by George McCready Price, dominated Adventist thought on the issue in the early 1900s. Price denied that the sequence was real, arguing that, contrary to the claims of conventional geology, fossil-bearing strata could be found in many different sequences. For example, geologists recognize a large area in Montana that displays Precambrian rocks on top of Cretaceous rocks. Geologists argue that these out-of-order sequences resulted from thrust faults—low-angle faults that develop when the crust is horizontally compressed, with rocks on one side pushed up and over rocks on the other side. Price was not impressed. describing thrust faults as hypothetical, "a pitiful example of the hypnotizing power of a false theory in the presence of the very plainest facts" (1923:627,629).

The first Seventh-day Adventist to publicly challenge Price's interpretation was Harold Clark, one of Price's former students who did graduate work in biology and taught at Pacific Union College. Clark initially taught Price's view but, when challenged by a student whose father was in the oil industry, Clark took the opportunity to see for himself by spending part of a summer in the oil fields examining strata. He came away convinced: the sequence of fossil-bearing strata was real (Numbers 2006:144).

Clark then drew on his ecological knowledge of the American West to offer a novel explanation for the fossil sequence. Perhaps, he reasoned, the world before the Flood had a complex ecology, with distinct communities along an elevational gradient from deep sea to high mountains, analogous to what you see today in mountainous regions of the West (Fig. 4). The fossil sequence, then, could be viewed as a gradually rising destruction-and-burial sequence; the Flood initially destroyed and buried habitats and organisms at low elevations and progressively inundated ever-higher habitats. If the pre-Flood world differed in having various "seas" at different elevations, this process might sort even marine creatures into stratigraphic "zones" (Clark 1940). (Remarkably similar ideas were developed, independently, in the early to mid-1800s [Cockburn 1849]).

Clark termed his theory Ecological Zonation, and it has remained a mainstay in textbook explanations of the fossil sequence by flood geologists (Coffin et al. 2005; Nichol 1978:87–89; Roth 1998). Roth, although noting some challenges, summarized features that he saw as consistent with the model: for example, the presence of microscopic life in deep rocks presumably deposited before the Flood (and subsequently invaded by microbes); the sudden appearance of complex marine life forms at the base of the Cambrian, suggesting the advent of Flood deposition in pre-Flood seas; and the roughly coordinated appearance of various groups of land organisms (fungi, various plant groups, insects and other terrestrial arthropods, land-dwelling vertebrates) in the Silurian and Devonian, perhaps laid down as the Flood began to inundate terrestrial habitats (Roth 1998).

Despite the prominence of Ecological Zonation theory in Adventist discussion of the fossil record, several authors have noted problems with the theory (Brand 2009; Ritland 2000; Roth 1998). For example, wind-blown pollen of flowering plants has been reported only in Cretaceous and higher strata. Today, winds widely disperse pollen, even into marine environments. If Cretaceous flowering plants that produced wind-blown pollen were alive in higher-elevation habitats at the same time as Upper Paleozoic lowland swamp forests, and there was at least moderate wind before the Flood, one might expect pollen to have been blown into the lowlands. In addition, the theory has seldom been applied to explain the stratigraphic

**Figure 4**—A pictorial model of Ecological Zonation as developed by Harold Clark. Reproduced by permission of the publisher from *Faith, Reason, and Earth History: A Paradigm of Earth and Biological Origins by Intelligent Design,* 2nd ed., by Leonard Brand. Copyright © 2009 by Andrews University Press.

distribution of specific taxa in the fossil record. In fact, when I surveyed the journal *Origins,* published by the GRI since 1975, I found only a single attempted explanation in over 30 years: a paper that noted some parallels between the fossil sequence of marine foraminiferans and the expectations of Ecological Zonation (Tosk 1988).

Flood geologists have described other factors that might contribute to sorting fossils in the stratigraphic record within a global flood, including the mobility and intelligence of organisms and differences in how carcasses float in water after death. In general, these mechanisms are viewed as secondary to Ecological Zonation. One study, based on a broad survey of the literature, noted that amphibian and reptile footprints often were abundant in lower stratigraphic levels whereas the bones of the same groups were more abundant in higher strata. The authors viewed this observation as consistent with expectations of flood geology—perhaps animals were active early in the Flood, leaving footprints, but subsequently died, leaving only carcasses to preserve as fossils (Brand and Florence 1982).

### *Evolutionary Interpretations*

Several Adventist creationists have briefly critiqued various transitional fossils (Brand 2009; Coffin et al. 2005; Roth 1998). For example, Read (2009) critiqued a fossil viewed as transitional to dinosaurs (*Marasuchus*) and judged it inadequate because it was substantially smaller than the earliest known dinosaur. In contrast, Adventist authors have emphasized the opposite pattern in the fossil record: the abrupt appearance of major groups in stratigraphic sequences, consistent with special creation of separate lineages. The classic example of this pattern, widely recognized in the scientific literature (e.g., Conway Morris 2000; Erwin et al. 1997; Valentine et al. 1999) and often discussed by Adventist authors (e.g., Coffin 1974; Gibson 2001; Roth 1998; 2008), is the Cambrian Explosion: the relatively abrupt appearance of most animal phyla with skeletons that can fossilize without clear ancestry. Of particular interest is the abrupt appearance of trilobites in the early Cambrian, which demonstrates that the complex molecular systems involved in cell division, neuron function, development, and vision were already in place—an argument for special creation (Chadwick and DeHaan 2000).

Although the Cambrian Explosion epitomizes abrupt appearance in the fossil sequence, the pattern shows up repeatedly in the record (but at lower taxonomic levels)—in various groups and within different geological intervals—a fact recognized by creationists and evolutionary paleontologists alike. Let us illustrate with fossil proboscideans. According to one review (not by creationists), the earliest proboscideans were "already quite specialized in some features" and "demonstrate an unexpected diversity" when they appear in the stratigraphic record, suggesting substantial time for earlier evolutionary changes not documented in the stratigraphic record. Similarly, these authors recognized a "significant morphological gap" between these early, primitive proboscideans and "the first elephantiforms," with the latter being much larger in size and "decidedly more elephantine in general aspect" (Gheerbrant et al. 2005:90). The authors attribute these abrupt appearances to a woefully incomplete fossil record—probably a reasonable argument in this case because very few early Cenozoic strata are known from Africa. However, Ariel Roth argued that an incomplete fossil record may not work as a general explanation for the abrupt appearance of taxa; many groups appear to be well represented in the fossil record (1998:188–189).

Finally, some authors have pointed to living fossils—lineages alive today that have a deep fossil record but exhibit very little change through the stratigraphic sequence—as potentially challenging for evolution. If the stratigraphic sequence represents millions of years, why do they persist over geological time without much change in form? As an example, Conrad Clausen, then at Loma Linda University, discussed a deep-ocean mollusk group, the monoplacophorans, which displays such a pattern. Some paleontologists attributed its morphological stability over geological time (Silurian-Recent) to long-term stability of deep-ocean environments, but subsequent work called this into question: the ocean deeps have not been stable across geological time (Clausen 1976).

In summary, one approach Seventh-day Adventist scholars have taken to answer the challenges of geological time, the fossil sequence, and large-scale evolution is to critique conventional interpretations and suggest alternative theories to account for what is observed. A second approach, discussed in the following section, has been to do research that attempts to address challenges and to explore the fossil record from a different perspective. This approach illustrates well a principle noted in chapter 1: that challenges in science—things we do not understand—may provide both motivation and direction for productive study.

## Seventh-day Adventist Research in Paleontology

Adventist scientists began to do serious, original research in paleontology during the 1970s, stimulated by a vision that research guided by biblical insights should "on the average," make "more frequent and/or significant advances in the understanding of the natural world" than research not guided by those insights (Neufeld 1974:12). Let us consider a few examples, which are placed in stratigraphic context in Figure 3.

During the 1960s, Adventist scientists and thought leaders became aware of a major challenge to Flood geology: an Eocene stratigraphic sequence with over 40 fossil forests, one above the other, preserved in the Yellowstone area of Wyoming and adjacent Montana, with each forest buried by volcanic debris.

Harold Coffin, who worked at GRI, took on the Yellowstone forests as a research problem. He published several studies in the standard scientific literature and argued that upright stumps usually interpreted as in-growth tree stumps may have been transported by volcanic debris. For example, vertical stumps with noncircular cross sections (that is, stumps with a clear long-axis due to oblong or similar shape) often showed a preferred orientation in a given level that matched the orientation of prostrate logs in the same levels, suggesting that both had been oriented by the dynamics of transport in volcanic mudflows (Coffin 1976). Further, studies of log debris dumped into Spirit Lake by the eruption of Mount St. Helens showed that stumps often floated upright in this debris, and that the upright stumps eventually sank to the bottom, perhaps suggesting a mechanism for getting upright stumps without growing a forest (Coffin 1983a; 1987). Coffin also published several papers in *Origins* on this work (1979; 1983b), culminating in a special issue that summarized his argument for transported logs and stumps (1997). His model appears to substantially alleviate the time problem presented by the stacked forests at Yellowstone.

A number of other Adventist scientists have contributed to the study of the Yellowstone forests. Consider Arthur Chadwick, a long-term contributor to Adventist research on earth history, who worked with a student to investigate fossil plants preserved at various forest levels (Chadwick and Yamamoto 1984). They observed that the plant assemblages were substantially mixed ecologically, and with different mixtures at different levels—consistent with a model that the plants were washed in from surrounding source areas.

Leonard Brand, a biologist at Loma Linda University and major contributor to Adventist Flood geology, addressed a creationist problem in a series of studies on vertebrate trackways from the Permian Coconino Sandstone of Arizona. Conventional geologists generally interpret the Coconino as having formed in a vast, ancient desert, but Brand found this puzzling: How do you get desert deposits in a sequence being laid down by the Flood? He tackled the problem by studying well-preserved trackways in the Coconino. Brand (1979) compared fossil trackways with those made by modern salamanders and lizards under various conditions, and he concluded that fossils most closely matched those made by salamanders walking under water. This paper was later reprinted as a benchmark paper in the study of fossil trackways (Brand 1983).

In a subsequent study, Brand focused on peculiar trackways preserved in the Coconino. For example, some trackways show that the animal was attempting to walk in one direction (as indicated by the direction of toes) but was in fact moving at right angles to that direction. These trackways closely matched some made by experimental salamanders walking in one direction while being pushed sideway by a gentle current (Brand and Tang 1991)—again suggesting underwater formation.

Other studies have not addressed specific problems but have explored themes that Flood geology suggests should be fruitful. For example, Raul Esperante, Leonard Brand, and several others have done significant work on Cenozoic strata in Peru that feature abundant, well-preserved fossil whales, sometimes so well preserved that the filter-feeding apparatus of these ancient giants remains in place (Esperante et al. 2008)! These studies demonstrate that the fossil whales were buried rapidly—even those buried by diatom-rich sediments that today accumulate very slowly (Brand et al. 2004).

Sometimes, however, careful studies done by Adventist scientists seem to suggest time challenges for Flood geology. Lance Hodges, a student of Ariel Roth, did a comparative study of Paleozoic, Pleistocene, and modern reefs. He noted that Paleozoic reefs differed from Pleistocene and modern reefs in that they had a much lower density of reef-forming organisms (Hodges 1987). Nonetheless, careful study of how organisms were oriented within the reefs showed that in several cases they were preserved in the orientation of natural growth (mostly vertical in the reef core); the reefs were not a washed-in jumble of fossils. The authors concluded that either 1) the reefs grew in place (which would take some time to occur); or 2) the whole reef structure was transported from elsewhere (Hodges and Roth 1986).

The studies noted above illustrate contributions that directly bear on concerns of Flood geology. In addition, Adventist scientists have contributed to a range of paleontological themes such as ancient ecology (e.g., Leggitt and Cushman 2001); biogeography (e.g., Goodwin 1995); and especially taphonomy—the study of what happens to organisms between death and potential fossilization (Brand et al. 2000; 2003; Esperante et al. 2008; Hayward 1991; Smith and Hayward 2010). Space forbids a comprehensive survey of published studies in paleontology by Adventist authors, but cases described above underscore the reality that Seventh-day Adventist scientists have made significant contributions to the discipline.

Clearly Seventh-day Adventist scientists have conducted creative research, often stimulated by the challenges posed by geology and paleontology. Some studies have made progress in solving apparent problems; others have fruitfully explored features of the fossil record, showing that some fossil-bearing strata accumulated rapidly; and still others highlight the need for better models to accommodate what we find in the rocks. Given that challenges persist, what alternative theories have Adventists proposed?

## Other Theories

Most Seventh-day Adventist study of the fossil record has been guided by the theory of Flood geology, as described above. A few Adventists, however, have explored other options, motivated by a desire to better account for what we see in nature while retaining a commitment to biblical truth. Let us now consider two examples.

Jack Provonsha, a physician and ethicist who worked for many years at Loma Linda University, tentatively offered a theory that has much in common with the so-called gap theory popular among Fundamentalists in the early 1900s. He suggested that the fossil record might represent the remains of a preceding creation, which Satan, after his expulsion from heaven, manipulated over eons to evolve the diverse forms we find in the record. When the principles of Satan's kingdom were clear for all to see, God stepped in and re-created the earth and life, in 6 days—a short time ago as recorded in Genesis (Provonsha 2000). This model attributes the predation, suffering, and death recorded by fossils to the work of Satan, and thus solves one theological difficulty of long-age creation models—why a good God would use such a process to create life. However, few Adventist authors have taken his model seriously: biblical support is weak, and fossil evidence does not document a gap between the proposed two creations.

A second attempt to offer a more satisfactory model was made by Leonard Brand. Brand termed his model *wholistic geology* because it attempted to take seriously insights from both nature and the Bible. In particular, Brand was struck by evidence for geological and paleontological events in the rock record that appear to require more than one year to form (see preceding section). He also reminded readers that the belief that most of the fossil record was laid down in a single year is an assumption, not a teaching of the Scriptures. In contrast, he suggested that perhaps substantial geological activity began after the Fall, accelerated during the Flood, and continued for some time after the Flood. In this model, the fossil-bearing rock record may have been laid down in centuries to a few millennia, giving more time to accommodate geological processes (Brand 2007). This model has not yet received significant attention by other Adventist scientists.

## Future Directions?

The fossil record has intrigued Seventh-day Adventist scientists and laypersons for over 100 years. The Adventist commitment to understand this record in light of biblical revelation has stimulated discussion, sparked development of new theories, and encouraged productive research. However, we have much to learn, so if you are considering a career in the field, take heart! If you are committed to learn and do rigorous science while being faithful to God's Word, the Church can use your talents to collect new data, test and improve existing theories, and come up with better ways to integrate our knowledge of the Bible and God's creation.

What types of research in paleobiology could be especially fruitful? Radiometric dating and other methods of geochronology deserve further study, as do the stratigraphic and geographic distribution of fossils, and the structure and relationships of transitional fossils. New fields of paleontology also may offer potential for fruitful investigation. For example, some paleontologists have reported the presence of complex biomolecules and cellular structures in dinosaur bone and other ancient fossils (e.g., Schweitzer et al. 2007a; 2007b; 2005). The circumstances that might allow such preservation are incompletely known and deserve further study, but one possibility is that the fossils are much younger than normally interpreted.

Meanwhile, consider an entirely different application for paleobiology: using it as stewards of creation to help us understand and better deal with the loss of biodiversity. This brings us back to the mastodons and mammoths of the Ice Age. Can we learn lessons from the extinction of these and many other large mammals near the end of the Ice Age that might help us understand and more effectively respond to the pressures leading to the decline of modern creatures—including elephants? Some paleontologists believe that we can, especially since some evidence links Ice Age extinctions to the combined effects of climate change and human pressure—similar to the pressures impinging on life's diversity today (Barnosky et al. 2004). This approach might help us better serve as stewards of God's creation, the first task humanity was given in the Garden of Eden (Genesis 1:28; 2:15). (We will return to the question of environmental stewardship in chapter 7.)

Finally, whether you are looking to a career in paleontology or related field, or simply wish to be an educated person who enjoys engaging the science-faith dialogue, I encourage you to reflect on—and apply—the principles suggested in chapter 1 for dealing with tension between science and faith. First, be faithful to God's Word; do not let science or any other way of knowing cause you to doubt this gift. Second, be faithful to the evidence of science, even when that evidence poses difficulties. It is often fruitful to reexamine the evidence as original authors might not have thought of some possibilities given their worldview commitments, but we must not claim answers to issues that are not actually resolved. Third, seek integration in a way that honors the first two principles—but do not force it. It is better to leave some questions unanswered, rather than to force inadequate answers! And above all, remember that Jesus calls us to love each other (John 13:35)—and this applies even (and perhaps especially!) when we debate how best to do the work of integrating faith and science.

## Literature Cited

Baldwin, J. T. 1991. Progressive creation and biblical revelation: Some theological implications. Origins 18:53–65.

Baldwin, J. T., ed. 2000. Creation, catastrophe, and Calvary: Why a global flood is vital to the doctrine of atonement. Review and Herald Publishing Association, Hagerstown, Maryland.

Barnosky, A. D., P. L. Koch, R. S. Feranec, S. L. Wing, and A. B. Shabel. 2004. Assessing the causes of Late Pleistocene extinctions on the continents. Science 306:70–75.

Benton, M. J. 1993. Fossil Record 2, 2nd ed. Chapman & Hall, London and New York.

Brand, L. R. 1979. Field and laboratory studies on the Coconino Sandstone (Permian) vertebrate footprints and their paleoecological implications. Palaeogeography, Palaeoclimatology, Palaeoecology 28:25–38.

Brand, L. R. 1983. Field and laboratory studies on the Coconino Sandstone (Permian) fossil vertebrate footprints and their paleoecological implications. Pp. 126–139 in Terrestrial trace fossils. Benchmark Papers in Geology (W. A. S. Sarjeant, ed.).

Brand, L. R. 2007. Wholistic geology: Geology before, during, and after the biblical flood. Origins 61:7–34.

Brand, L. R. 2009. Faith, reason, and earth history, 2nd ed. Andrews University Press, Berrien Springs, Michigan.

Brand, L. R., H. T. Goodwin, P. D. Ambrose, and H. P. Buchheim. 2000. Taphonomy of turtles in the middle Eocene Bridger Formation, SW Wyoming. Palaeogeography, Palaeoclimatology, Palaeoecology 162:171–189.

Brand, L., and J. Florence. 1982. Stratigraphic distribution of vertebrate fossil footprints compared with body fossils. Origins 9:67–74.

Brand, L. R., M. Hussey, and J. Taylor. 2003. Decay and disarticulation of small vertebrates in controlled experiments. Journal of Taphonomy 1:69–95.

Brand, L. R., R. Esperante, A. V. Chadwick, O. Poma Porras, and M. Alomía. 2004. Fossil whale preservation implies high diatom accumulation rate in the Miocene-Pliocene Pisco Formation of Peru. Geology 32:165–168.

Brand, L. R., and T. Tang. 1991. Fossil vertebrate footprints in the Coconino Sandstone (Permian) of Northern Arizona: Evidence for underwater origin. Geology 19:1201–1204.

Brown, R. H. 1977. Radiometric age and the traditional Hebrew-Christian view of time. Origins 4:68–85.

Brown, R. H. 1979. The interpretation of C-14 dates. Origins 6:30–44.

Brown, R. H. 1981. Geo and cosmic chronology. Origins 8:20–45.

Brown, R. H. 1988. The upper limit of C-14 age? Origins 15:39–43.

Brown, R. H. 1990. Correlation of C-14 age with the biblical time scale. Origins 17:56–65.
Carroll, R. L. 1997. Patterns and processes of vertebrate evolution. Cambridge University Press, Cambridge, United Kingdom.
Chadwick, A., and T. Yamamoto. 1984. A paleoecological analysis of the petrified trees in the Specimen Creek area of Yellowstone National Park, Montana, U.S.A. Palaeogeography Palaeoclimatology Palaeoecology 45:39–48.
Chadwick, A. V., and R. F. Dehaan. 2000. The trilobite: Enigma of complexity. A case for intelligent design. Perspectives on Science and Christian Faith 52:233–241.
Clark, H. W. 1940. Genes and Genesis. Pacific Press, Mountain View, California.
Clausen, C. D. 1976. *Neopilina*: A living fossil. Origins 3:56–59.
Cockburn, W. 1849. A new system of geology. Henry Colburn, London.
Coffin, H. G. 1974. Famous fossils from a mountaintop. Origins 1:45–47.
Coffin, H. G. 1976. Orientation of trees in the Yellowstone petrified forests. Journal of Paleontology 50:539–543.
Coffin, H. G. 1979. The organic levels of the Yellowstone petrified forests. Origins 6:71–82.
Coffin, H. G. 1983a. Erect floating stumps in Spirit Lake, Washington. Geology 11:298–299.
Coffin, H. G. 1983b. Mount St. Helens and Spirit Lake. Origins 10:9–17.
Coffin, H. G. 1987. Sonar and scuba survey of a submerged allochthonous "forest" in Spirit Lake, Washington. Palaios 2:178–180.
Coffin, H. G. 1997. The Yellowstone petrified "forests." Origins 24:5–44.
Coffin, H. G., R. H. Brown, and L. J. Gibson. 2005. Origin by design, Revised ed. Review and Herald Publishing Association, Hagerstown, MD.
Collins, F. S. 2006. The language of God: A scientist presents evidence for belief. Free Press, New York.
Conway Morris, S. 2000. The Cambrian "explosion": Slow-fuse or megatonnage? Proceedings of the National Academy of Sciences 97:4426–4429.
Davidson, R. M. 2003. The biblical account of origins. Journal of the Adventist Theological Society 14:4–43.
Erwin, D., J. Valentine, and D. Jablonski. 1997. The origin of animal body plans. American Scientist 85:126–137.

Esperante, R., L. Brand, K. E. Nick, O. Poma, and M. Urbina. 2008. Exceptional occurrence of fossil baleen in shallow marine sediments of the Neogene Pisco Formation, Southern Peru. Palaeogeography, Palaeoclimatology, Palaeoecology 257:344–360.

Falk, D. R. 2004. Coming to peace with science: Bridging the worlds between faith and biology. InterVarsity Press, Downers Grove, Illinois.

Gheerbrant, E., D. P. Domning, and P. Tassy. 2005. Paenungulata (Sirenia, Proboscidea, Hyracoidea, and relatives). Pp. 84–105 in The rise of placental mammals: Origins and relationships of the major extant clades. The Johns Hopkins University Press, Baltimore.

Gibson, L. J. 2001. Polyphyly and the Cambrian explosion. Origins 52:3–6.

Giem, P. 1997. Scientific theology. La Sierra University Press, Riverside, California.

Giem, P. 2001. Carbon-14 content of fossil carbon. Origins 51:6–30.

Goodwin, H. T. 1995. Pliocene-Pleistocene biogeographic history of prairie dogs, genus *Cynomys* (Sciuridae). Journal of Mammalogy 76:100–122.

Hasel, G. F. 1994. The "Days" of creation in Genesis 1: Literal "days" or figurative "periods/epochs" of time? Origins 21:5–38.

Hayward, J. L. 1991. Rapid dissolution of avian eggshells buried by Mount St. Helens ash. Palaios 6:174–178.

Hayward, J. L. 1993a. Dinosaurs. Adventist Review, August 12, pp. 12–14.

Hayward, J. L. 1993b. Noah's Ark or "Jurassic Park"? Spectrum 23(2):6–14.

Hodges, L. T. 1987. Fossil binding in modern and ancient reefs. Origins 14:84–91.

Hodges, L. T., and A. A. Roth. 1986. Orientation of corals and stromatoporoids in some Pleistocene, Devonian, and Silurian reef facies. Journal of Paleontology 60:1147–1158.

Holman, J. A. 2001. In quest of Great Lakes Ice Age vertebrates. Michigan State University Press, East Lansing, Michigan.

Jell, P. A., and J. M. Adrain. 2002. Available generic names for trilobites. Memoirs of the Queensland Museum 48:331–553.

Johns, W. H. 2008. Scriptural geology, 1820–1860: an essay and review. Origins 62:42–60.

Lambert, W. D., and J. Shoshani. 1998. Proboscidea. Pp. 606–621 in Evolution of Tertiary mammals of North America (C. M. Janis, K. M.

Scott and L. L. Jacobs, eds.). Cambridge University Press, Cambridge, United Kingdom.

Leggitt, V. L., and R. A. Cushman. 2001. Complex caddisfly-dominated bioherms from the Eocene Green River Formation. Sedimentary Geology 145:377–396.

Lister, A. M., and P. Bahn. 2007. Mammoths: giants of the ice age. Revised edition. University of California Press, Berkeley, California.

Neufeld, B. R. 1974. Towards the development of a general theory of creation. Origins 1:6–13.

Nichol, F. D., ed. 1978. Seventh-day Adventist Bible Commentary. Vol. 1. Review and Herald Publishing Association, Washington, DC.

Niedzwiedzki, G., P. Szrek, K. Narkiewicz, M. Narkiewicz, and P. E. Ahlberg. 2010. Tetrapod trackways from the early Middle Devonian period of Poland. Nature 463:43–48.

Numbers, R. L. 2006. The creationists: From scientic creationism to intelligent design, Expanded ed. Harvard University Press, Cambridge, Massachusetts.

Price, G. M. 1923. The new geology. Pacific Press Publishing Association, Mountain View, California.

Prothero, D. R. 2007. Evolution: What the fossils say and why it matters. Columbia University Press, New York.

Prothero, D. R., and R. M. Schoch. 2002. Horns, tusks, and flippers: The evolution of hoofed mammals. The Johns Hopkins University Press, Baltimore.

Provonsha, J. W. 2000. The creation/evolution debate in light of the Great Controversy. Pp. 303–311 in Creation reconsidered: Scientific, biblical, and theological perspectives (J. L. Hayward, ed.). Association of Adventist Forums, Roseville, California.

Ramm, B. 1954. The Christian view of science and scripture. Wm. B. Eerdmans, Grand Rapids, Michigan.

Read, D. C. 2009. Dinosaurs: An Adventist view. Clarion Call Books, Keene, Texas.

Ritland, R. M. 2000. Ecological zonation theory. Pp. 145–181 in Creation reconsidered: Scientific, biblical, and theological perspectives (J. L. Hayward, ed.). Association of Adventist Forums, Roseville, California.

Roth, A. A. 1986. Some questions about geochronology. Origins 13:64–85.

Roth, A. A. 1988. Those gaps in the sedimentary layers. Origins 15:75–92.

Roth, A. A. 1992. Life in the deep rocks and the deep fossil record. Origins 19:93–104.

Roth, A. A. 1995. Fossil reefs and time. Origins 22:86–104.

Roth, A. A. 1998. Origins: linking science and scripture. Review and Herald Publishing Association, Hagerstown, Maryland.

Roth, A. A. 2008. Science discovers God: Seven convincing lines of evidence for his existence. Review and Herald Publishing Association, Hagerstown, Maryland.

Schweitzer, M. H., et al. 2007a. Analyses of soft tissue from *Tyrannosaurus rex* suggest the presence of protein. Science 316:277–280.

Schweitzer, M. H., J. L. Wittmeyer, and J. R. Horner. 2007b. Soft tissue and cellular preservation in vertebrate skeletal elements from the Cretaceous to the present. Proceedings of the Royal Society (B) 274:183–197.

Schweitzer, M. H., J. L. Wittmeyer, J. R. Horner, and J. K. Toporski. 2005. Soft-tissue vessels and cellular preservation in *Tyrannosaurus rex*. Science 307:1952–1955.

Smith, D. L., and J. L. Hayward. 2010. Bacterial decomposition of avian eggshell: A taphonomic experiment. Palaios 25:318–326.

Tosk, T. 1988. Foraminifers in the fossil record: Implications for an ecological zonation model. Origins 15:8–18.

Valentine, J. W., D. Jablonski, and D. H. Erwin. 1999. Fossils, molecules and embryos: New perspectives on the Cambrian explosion. Developmental Psychobiology. 126:851–859.

Wang, S. C., and P. Dodson. 2006. Estimating the diversity of dinosaurs. Proceedings of the National Academy of Sciences 103:13601–13605.

White, E. G. 1864a. Spiritual gifts, vol. III. Steam Press of the Seventh-day Adventist Publishing Association, Battle Creek, Michigan.

White, E. G. 1864b. Spiritual gifts, vol. IV. Steam Press of the Seventh-day Adventist Publishing Association, Battle Creek, Michigan.

## Chapter Six

# AN ADVENTIST VIEW OF ECOLOGY

**David L. Cowles**

Ecology is the study of the interaction of living things with the living and nonliving elements of their environment. With such a broad definition, almost anything that humans do could be subsumed within ecology. This chapter, however, will be more specific and explore Christian and specifically Adventist perspectives on the processes that govern the interactions among humans, other living things, and their environment. I will spend little time discussing protection of the environment, as important as that issue is, because that topic is covered in chapter 7. This essay will simply discuss unique perspectives that I, as an Adventist Christian, have on how the earth works and why it works that way. It will also examine several areas in which views common among Adventists seem in conflict with scientific observations, together with an exploration of some ecological questions and puzzles posed by a biblical worldview.

### A Core Difference in Perspective: The Earth as the Lord's Handiwork

For the most part and in day-to-day work, there is very little difference between an Adventist view of ecology and that of any other ecologist. The topics and focus in my classes and the types of questions I choose for research are very similar to what one could find in any good textbook or research program. The differences my Adventist perspective brings to the study of ecology stem mostly from my having a view of the world that is somewhat different from that of my secular colleagues.

One of the most important differences between a biblical Adventist view of ecology and the mechanistic one most commonly advocated in science comes from the biblical teaching that God personally created the earth and its living things, that it was all for a divine purpose, and that God's will is the final cause. "The earth is the LORD's, and the fulness thereof, the world, and they that dwell therein" (Psalm 24:1).[1] "[T]he LORD that created the heavens; God himself that formed the earth and made it; he hath established it, he created it not in vain, he formed it to be inhabited" (Isaiah 45:18). "Thou art worthy, O Lord, to receive glory and honour and power: for thou hast created all things, and for thy pleasure they are and were created" (Revelation 4:11). "For in six days the LORD made heaven and earth, the sea, and all that in them is" (Exodus 20:11). Further, the Bible tells us that humankind was created with a special status, given dominion over the earth and its creatures (Genesis 1:28; Psalm 8:6), and given a special commission as a steward to "dress it and to keep it" (Genesis 2:15).

The idea of a purpose or final cause for life on the earth, including human life, is known as teleology. Mainstream science, which insists on a strictly naturalistic approach, actively avoids or limits teleology (Mayr 1992; Reiss 2007; Edin 2008) because it does not appear to be directly testable and implies a cause outside of the observable data. Certainly, even Christian scientists must avoid the cavalier conclusion that "God did it" when studying hard-to-understand natural phenomena. Such an approach can prematurely end inquiry and lead to satisfaction with inadequate answers. Christian scientists will focus on mechanistic explanations for observed processes in nature because we believe that God's ultimate control of nature often works itself out through the operation of the laws of nature that He created (a concept discussed in chapter 1).

Ellen White directly supported this empirical approach to understanding the way nature works. "God is continually working through [the laws of nature], using them as His instruments. They are not self-working. God is perpetually at work in nature" (1948:259–260). This statement could on the surface be taken to mean that nature's workings are inscrutable except to God. However, she clarifies those statements by other statements such as, "God works through the calm, regular operation of His appointed laws" (1946:139–140), implying that our approach first should be to look for explanations based on regular laws and physical principles rather than invoking miracles.

The Christian commitment to teleology, however, recognizes that God sometimes acts in more direct ways—ways that go beyond the random outworking of natural laws. We believe that God works through nature

1. All Scripture quotations (unless otherwise noted) are taken from the King James Version.

and that His creation was "very good" (Genesis 1:31), thus we expect to find orderly function as a pervasive principle. We expect the world to make sense, to follow rational principles—even for phenomena that resist explanation by simple mechanistic means, such as the origin of complex structures and information-rich instruction codes in living things. For that reason I believe that the concepts of irreducible complexity and intelligent design advocated by the intelligent design movement (Denton 1986; Behe 1996; Dembski 1999) are valid and exciting fields of inquiry for the Christian scientist, if carried out correctly. Unlike the strict naturalists, who must limit investigation to consider only undirected mechanistic explanations for all phenomena, no matter how wildly improbable those explanations might be, Christian scientists should be free to expand their set of hypotheses to include direct divine input—but only if the natural processes affecting a phenomenon are well understood and the likelihood of purely mechanistic explanations can be shown to be negligible. Note clearly that this does not mean that complexity itself warrants hypothesizing divine interference, but if the natural processes affecting a phenomenon are well understood and it can be shown that the likelihood for these processes alone being sufficient to produce the observed phenomenon is very small, then a Christian scientist should be free to consider the hypothesis that the phenomenon results at least partly from direct divine action rather than solely from mechanistic means.

If God created the earth to sustain life, we would expect to find that conditions on earth are designed for that purpose (although subsequent degradation of creation may have marred this design). The idea that the universe appears to be fine-tuned for life is known as the anthropic principle. Evidence for fine-tuning is abundant, and can be found at every level of organization. Physicists, for example, note the precise balancing of the four fundamental forces. They calculate that if either the strong or weak nuclear forces were a few percent stronger, the nuclear furnaces of stars (the site of element formation in current scientific models) would yield primarily heavy elements and only a trace of the element hydrogen, which is necessary for life. If the forces were weaker, nuclei would not hold together, everything would be hydrogen, and life would not be possible. If the mass ratios and numbers of protons, neutrons, and electrons were not precisely balanced with one another to within a fraction of a percent of what they are, chemical bonds would not readily form, stars would collapse into black holes, and galaxies would not form (Ross 1993; Roth 2008). Astronomers note that if the average distance between stars and galaxies were much greater or less, either planets would not have appropriate conditions to form or they would experience conditions hostile to life. Even extreme phenomena such as supernovae and white dwarf stars have a part to play in the balance of the universe (Ross 1993). Truly, as David noted, "The heavens declare the glory of God" (Psalm 19:1), in more ways than even he imagined!

The fine-tuning for life does not stop with the distant universe and the fundamental laws of physics. The earth itself seems intricately specialized to sustain life (Roth 2008). Our sun is the correct size and the earth-sun distance is right to produce an optimum range of temperatures for life. The earth's rotation provides a relatively moderate climate without deadly extremes of heat and cold. The earth is sufficiently large to retain water in the atmosphere, yet not so large that high levels of toxic ammonia and methane are also retained. The atmosphere contains sufficient water vapor, carbon dioxide, and methane to trap outgoing radiation and keep earth's average temperature above freezing, but not so much that the surface is a boiling inferno as on some other planets. The large amount of water on the surface absorbs and distributes heat efficiently and provides an abundant habitat for living things, but water does not cover the entire surface—continental areas remain for terrestrial life. The moon provides tidal circulation of the ocean but is not so large or so close that tidal forces become devastatingly destructive. All the elements necessary for life occur in abundance on the earth's surface. Readily available solar energy drives energy fixation via photosynthesis, yet the atmosphere screens out most of the DNA-damaging ultraviolet radiation. Temperatures of most of the earth's surface remain within a suitable range fully supportive of life. A variety of food sources are available in most habitats. Food chains are generally well balanced with an abundance of primary producers that support a variety of consumers, yet the consumers do not overwhelm the producers. This balance is so consistent across habitats on earth that one favorite discussion topic in ecological textbooks is, Why is the earth green? There are a few places on earth where conditions are so severe or resources so limited that only a depauperate community exists (Chivian et al. 2008), but those habitats are surprisingly rare—the vast majority of the earth's surface supports an abundance of life. In general the biosphere is teeming with life and well provided for. It does appear that God abundantly provides for the sparrows (Matthew 10:29)—not only for their food but also their entire ecosystem—and for a vast number of other species as well.

A biblically informed perspective of life on earth recognizes that God is the Author and Sustainer of created things. It rejects the position that nature is autonomous, meaningless, and run entirely by physical laws, while avoiding the opposite error—that God is in nature itself, that nature is God. Creation is by God but is not the same as God (Gunton 2002). God created something separate from Himself. Creation runs according to physical laws, which include mechanisms for survival. At Creation, God gave a commission for semiautonomous action when He said, "Be fruitful and multiply" (Genesis 1:22,28). Such autonomy could even logically include provision for change (such as microevolution) as organisms adjust to new circumstances (see discussion in chapter 4), providing earth's ecosystems with robustness and resilience.

## Death before Sin?

Even a cursory reading of the biblical account suggests that ecological relationships before the entry of sin were radically different from what we experience now. One central biblical theme is that death is a result of sin and did not exist before humans sinned. Paul writes, "by one man sin entered into the world, and death by sin" (Romans 5:12), and "The wages of sin is death, but the gift of God is eternal life through Jesus Christ our Lord" (Romans 6:23). These texts could be interpreted as referring specifically to humans, but other passages suggest that the whole world was affected by death and decay when sin entered. "The whole creation groaneth and travaileth in pain together until now" (Romans 8:22). "[T]he creation itself will be liberated from its bondage to decay" (Romans 8:21, NIV). In the new earth, which is often regarded as a restoration of God's original plan, "There will be no more death or mourning or crying or pain" (Revelation 21:4, NIV).

As I view the function of earth's ecosystems today with an ecologist's eye, I can hardly conceive of how ecosystems could function without death. The flow of energy and cycling of materials through trophic levels, which are the core processes of modern ecosystems, depend upon death. Both the predation and detrital food chains, so central to the function of most ecosystems, would halt without death, and nutrients would be tied up irreversibly in existing biomass. As a consequence, the entire system would come to a grinding halt with no further opportunity for growth or reproduction. Rapid development of starvation conditions for all but the primary producers could be expected. How, then, could the original creation have functioned without death?

I see several possible solutions to this dilemma. First, perhaps the "death" that Scripture refers to as appearing after sin applies only to humans (Terreros 2003). As possible support for this position, the context of nearly all of Paul's statements about death following sin suggest that he refers primarily to sin's effect on humans. Also, any biologist knows that fruit is composed of living cells, and any eating of fruit in the Garden would necessarily entail the death of those cells unless the whole eating process was fundamentally different from what it is now. Since humans and animals were instructed to eat freely of fruit, it can be inferred that the type of death that fruit experiences is not the death which came by sin.

A similar but less radical view would be that "death" refers to the death of animals only (including humans) or even just to higher animals, but did not apply to plants, protists, or prokaryotes (Brand 2003). This view is broadly consistent with many aspects of the biblical story. For example, no death of any animal is referred to before sin, and there is no indication that Adam and Eve knew how to kill an animal until God prepared animal skins for their clothing, presumably from sacrificial animals (Genesis 3:21). The sacrificed lamb symbolized the death that was the result of sin, plus the future substitutionary death of the Savior. I am not aware of any reference in the Bible that describes the death of a plant (or bacteria, protist, or fungus) in the same terms it uses for animals. Indeed, the repeated Bible references to the idea that "the life is in the blood" (Genesis 9:4; Leviticus 17:11) may imply that only animals have the type of life spoken of. Regarding plant death in a different way from animal death would remove the problem of how Adam and Eve could eat fruit without causing death. Further, Scripture refers to New Earth conditions in terms that clearly suggest plant death. The lion that "eats straw like the lamb" is, frankly, consuming dead grass unless the straw is artificially manufactured from nonliving materials to look like grass, and what would be the point of that? If animals are going to eat artificially created foods for all time, why not produce "vegemeat" gazelles and zebras, or the legendary "tofudebeest" of *The Far Side* cartoon for the lion?

A third and more simplistic view would be that death did not exist for any of God's creation before sin, whether plant, animal, or bacteria. This view likely carries a satisfaction with it for many, since it envisions a world that would seem "very good," and it is certainly consistent with some of the direct statements of the Scriptures, though it seems to contradict the statements that animals ate plants in Eden. It also fits Ellen White's description that Adam and Eve were disheartened when they discovered fading flowers and wilting leaves that resulted from their sin (1890:62). As noted before, however, this view presents serious problems for biologists seeking to understand the ecology in that perfect world. It would have functioned totally differently from how ecosystems function today—even in fundamental processes such as eating by humans and all other biological consumers.

While some biblical support can be found for each of these three perspectives, I find the second perspective—that at least limited plant, cell, and bacterial death likely occurred as a natural function before sin—to be most consistent with the combination of biblical testimony and natural evidence. Efficient ecological processes with rapid, natural decay, the recycling of harvested plant materials, and the absence of disease could represent a divine plan for ecosystem function without requiring animal death. Abundant scientific evidence supports the fundamental role of nutrient recycling (including some death) in ecology, and I suspect that these processes likely reflect the original design. The incredibly diverse, intricately interconnected community of bacterial and fungal decomposers, and even the insects and worms that start the process of recycling, seem to be purposely and effectively designed for efficient breakdown and recycling of decomposing material. What would such communities do before sin, if there were no material to recycle? Postulating that these functions arose after sin requires radical change to several biotic kingdoms and genetic reprogramming of intricately connected physiological systems and metabolic pathways involved in nutrient recycling. Although such changes are possible, my observations of God's working leads me to think that He made these systems "very good," and then used them for efficient decomposition functions analogous to what we see today.

Other lines of evidence also suggest that limited death may be a natural, designed process. I will mention two. Programmed within each cell of our bodies is a specific, detailed pathway for the orderly shutdown and disintegration of the cell should the need arise (Gupta 2003). This process, called apoptosis, differs fundamentally from what happens when a cell is overwhelmed with external insults and falls apart in an uncontrolled manner. Instead, apoptosis often starts in an apparently healthy cell. In response to some condition or command, the cell transcribes genes whose products shut down the cell's survival and repair processes, chop up the DNA and nucleus, detach and isolate the cell from its neighbors, then break open the cell for final destruction by the body's housekeeping system (Earnshaw et al. 1999). In other words, this is an orderly, carefully executed suicide that seems to have been thoughtfully laid out and planned.

Sometimes apoptosis occurs as a response to cellular damage such as the DNA breakage which occurs during sunburn, but at other times it seems to be an integral part of normal body function. During fetal development, for example, many cells and groups of cells perform their function and then go through apoptosis to make room for the next process. Our hands form originally as paddles, then the cells in the webs between the fingers go through apoptosis to form the fully functional hand. Those rare occasions when apoptosis does not fully take place and the infant is born with webbed hands are regarded as birth defects. Knockout mice—genetically engineered mice—with various portions of the apoptosis pathway blocked frequently have growth abnormalities (Los et al. 1999). Why would God institute such a detailed process, intimately involved with the very formation of our bodies, *after sin* if the original process was "very good"? My tentative conclusion is that the intricate process of apoptosis itself is very good, and, as a corollary, certain types of death in limited circumstances were part of the original plan.

As a second example, entire plant organs such as leaves and fruits are doomed by orderly, genetically programmed, hormonally coordinated shutdown processes such as abscission (e.g., Price et al. 2008). Abscission is a process with both active and passive elements, which uses structural features which were strategically placed during the growth of the organ. Near the base of the leaf or fruit stem is an abscission zone. In this zone the cells are similar to those found elsewhere, but they are more metabolically active and may have slightly different shapes. When the fruit ripens or before leaf drop, a series of metabolic actions takes place. In response to an interconnecting set of signals from at least three different plant hormones (auxin, abscissic acid, and ethylene), cells in the abscission zone begin to modify their structure. In one region the cells step up production of the enzymes pectinase and cellulase. These enzymes are moved to their cell walls where they begin thinning and weakening the connections within the wall. The glue-like middle lamella which fastens cells tightly to one another is enzymatically dissolved. The weakened areas are oriented in such a way that a fracture line develops across the stem except for in the epidermal (surface) cells and the xylem (central conducting) cells. Meanwhile, adjacent cells adjust their internal osmotic pressure and swell, producing stress in the fracture line and propagating the crack further. Cells on the plant side of the abscission layer pack themselves full of a variety of compounds which seal off the stem and protect it from loss of water or entry of disease. All these processes are active metabolic processes in living cells, fueled by extra starch which was previously stored in this region. Finally, the stem is so weakened that gravity or wind causes the discarded leaf or ripe fruit to passively sever from the plant and drop to the ground, leaving a smooth, sealed scar behind (Coder 1999).

These examples suggest that at least cells and plants, rather than originally existing in a challenge-free, eternally safe, unchanging environment, were designed from the beginning to deal effectively with external challenges and the processing and even reprocessing of materials. This does not prove that cell death, reprocessing of cell materials, and the shedding of plant organs existed in the original plan—after all, these systems could have been preprogrammed as a response should sin eventually change the way things worked. However, it would at least seem to leave the idea open as a possibility. Could it even be the simplest (most parsimonious) scientific hypothesis?

Although I favor the arguments given above, I would not dismiss the possibility that the original ecology on earth functioned totally differently than we observe today. After all, we really do "see through a glass, darkly" (1 Corinthians 13:12), and our understanding of primeval ecology is limited. I am indebted to Leonard Brand for the following analogy: Reconstructing original ecology from what we see today is like coming across an old, dilapidated house and trying to understand its original condition when we have never seen a house before. Part of the house has been struck by lightning, and another part was carried away in a landslide. The roof blew off decades ago. Rain has soaked the contents inside for years and pooled on the floor. A sink hangs crazily from a wall with bent pipes attached. We try to use logic and our observations of this house to understand what its original systems were like. Some of our conclusions will be correct (e.g., maybe we notice that water that falls into the sink makes it out the drain); others will be wrong (the pools of water on the floor were never part of the original plan); and some things we miss completely (e.g., where did the water for this house come from?). Some things we may find by further study (such as finding water pipes underground that were not carried away by the landslide), and some may never be answered except by speculation.

The point of this analogy is this: We should be humble about what we think we know about the original creation. We have only a sketchy understanding about how ecosystems work today, as evidenced by the failure of the Biosphere 2 experiments despite millions of dollars of investment (Mervis 2003). In my view, we must continue to think and investigate creatively but remain honestly skeptical about our own opinions, generous and thoughtful about those of others, and always true to the Scriptures.

While considering how energy and materials could pass through ecosystems without death, it is enlightening to remember cooperative ecological interactions among species even today in which large amounts of energy and nutrients are passed back and forth without the death of either participant. As an example, consider nutritional symbioses between dinoflagellates (called zooxanthellae) or green algae (called zoochlorellae) and a variety of hosts such as corals, anemones, flatworms, giant clams, and nudibranchs (Rowan and Powers 1991; McNally et al. 1994). The symbionts live within the cells or in the hemocoel of their hosts, and are distributed in the host's body to maximize exposure to sunlight. When exposed to the sun, the symbionts fix carbon by photosynthesis. Much of the fixed carbon is exported out of the symbiont cells and taken up by the host (Engebretson and Muller-Parker 1999; Cantin et al. 2009). For most symbioses, the main exports are carbohydrates and lipids, and the host may need to obtain proteins from other sources (Ishikura et al. 1999). Evidence is strong, however, that the symbiotic algae also take up nitrogenous wastes from the host and resynthesize amino acids from them, some of which are returned to the host (Roberts et al. 1999; Wang and Douglas 1999). The host in turn provides a stable environment for the symbionts as well as ready access to light and raw materials. Neither party is consumed in the relationship, and both are benefitted. Perhaps interactions of this type were more prevalent in the past and may provide some insight into what might have been a common and widespread ecological relationship on earth prior to the Fall.

## Puzzling Ecological Aspects of the Biblical Description of the Original Creation

Biblical descriptions suggest other puzzling aspects of the original ecological systems. For example, the hydrological cycle seems to have been markedly different. The book of Genesis depicts an ecosystem with no rain (2:5) that was watered by mists or streams (2:6). A few ecosystems today are primarily watered by mist, including some tropical mountain forests. Most such ecosystems occur in deserts or semideserts with limited water supply, such as the Atacama desert of Peru or the Vizcaino desert of Baja California, where mists are generated from the adjacent cold ocean waters. We do not have a model for how this could occur on a large scale and result in a verdant ecosystem. Perhaps the closest example is the tropical cloud forest of Costa Rica. That model falls short as well, however, because the Edenic water source was clearly more than just a little mist. It produced an entire river that flowed from Eden and forked into four major branches. The New International Version, in fact, interprets "mist" in Genesis 2:6 as "streams." The source for these streams is unclear—perhaps there was some kind of hyporheic, or underground, flow.

Currently groundwater and hyporheic flow come from nearby—current or past—precipitation that deposits water onto an upland region of high potential energy. Gravity then produces the flow back to the ocean, including hyporheic flow. What energy source supplied the potential energy to raise the water supply to a place where it could flow back down to form the river? What route other than clouds and precipitation would move it to the highlands? In this case we literally need to find the "hidden water pipe" from my illustration above. Perhaps the "fountains of the great deep" (Genesis 7:11) played a role in this process.

Consider one more ecological puzzle. The biblical description of the early earth seems to depict a place of warm, even climate, at least near the Garden of Eden. The Garden flourished with vegetation, and Adam and Eve had no clothing. In that regard, it is interesting to note that a surprisingly large portion of the fossil record suggests communities living in much warmer conditions than exist in those areas today. Perhaps fossil evidence could shed further insights into global temperature distribution on the early earth.

## A Balanced Perspective on the Natural World

Finally, I believe Adventist Christians can offer one more valuable philosophical perspective on ecology. A shift has occurred over the past two centuries in how nature is regarded. Earlier perspectives regarded the natural world as a wondrous, almost miraculous network of entities helping one another. The brook took from the sky to give to the plants, which gave to the animals, which gave to humans, and so on. The eclipse of theistic considerations in science and the rise of the modern, mechanistic viewpoint have led to a very different perspective often referred to as the "survival of the fittest"—nature "red in tooth and claw," with each individual striving exclusively for its own benefit to the total exclusion of selection for benefit to any other. The evolutionary and sociobiological debates against the existence of genuine altruism are prime examples of this viewpoint. The ideas of kin selection, reciprocal altruism, and game theory admittedly have provided important insights into why certain altruistic-appearing characteristics occur in some species and situations but not in others. However, I believe that a simple, mechanistic view of "nature red in tooth and claw" is a distorted caricature of God's creation that in the beginning was "very good"—and that He still cares for. While the behavior of most species most of the time may be explicable in terms of direct benefits to the individual, I am struck by how often the suites of behaviors across all species in a community mesh in such a way that they yield a stable ecological system—one that benefits all. Perhaps that is God's way to ensure that core aspects of His original plan are worked out despite the prevalence of sin and selfishness. Note that some leaders in sociobiology have begun to point out that adaptive value to the individual is not necessarily the only way selection can work—benefits to the group (group selection) can also be important in some instances (Wilson and Wilson 2008).

In summary, an Adventist view of ecology is congruent with that of any other ecologist in many respects. Adventists can bring unique perspectives to the table, however, in ways that can benefit our understanding of God's creation, guide decisions we make about how to relate to the natural world, and provide valuable balance to the advancement of the science. Surely there are many important areas of interaction and different viewpoints that have not been addressed here. Now let us move forward—and continue the discussion!

## Literature Cited

Behe, M. J. 1996. Darwin's black box: The biochemical challenge to evolution. The Free Press, New York.

Brand, L. 2003. What are the limits of death in paradise? Journal of the Adventist Theological Society 14:74–85.

Cantin, N. E., M. J. H. van Oppen, B. L. Willis, J. C. Mieog, and A. P. Negri. 2009. Juvenile corals can acquire more carbon from high-performance algal symbionts. Coral Reefs 28:405–414.

Chivian, D. et al. 2008. Environmental genomics reveals a single-species ecosystem deep within earth. Science 322:275–278.

Coder, K. D. 1999. Falling tree leaves: Leaf abscission. The University of Georgia Daniel B. Warnell School of Forest Resources, the United States Department of Agriculture, and County Extension Agency Publication FOR99–025.

Dembski, W. A. 1999. Intelligent design: The bridge between science and theology. InterVarsity Press, Downer's Grove, Illinois.

Denton, M. 1986. Evolution: A theory in crisis. Adler & Adler Publishers, Bethesda, Maryland.

Earnshaw, W. C., L. M. Martins, and S. H. Kaufmann. 1999. Mammalian caspases: Structure, activation, substrates, and functions during apoptosis. Annual Review of Biochemistry 68:383–424.

Edin, B. B. 2008. Assigning biological functions: Making sense of causal chains. Synthese 161:203–218.

Engebretson, H. P. and G. Muller-Parker. 1999. Translocation of photosynthetic carbon from two algal symbionts to the sea anemone *Anthopleura elegantissima.* Biological Bulletin 197:72–81.

Gunton, C. E. 2001. The Christian faith: An introduction to Christian doctrine. Blackwell Publishers, Malden, Massachusetts.

Gupta, S. 2003. Molecular signaling in death receptor and mitochondrial pathways of apoptosis (review). International Journal of Oncology 22:15–20.

Ishikura, M., K. Adachi, and T. Maruyana. 1999. Zooxanthellae release glucose in the tissue of a giant clam, *Tridacna crocea.* Marine Biology 133:665–673.

Los, M., S. Wesselborg, and K. Schulze-Osthoff. 1999. The role of caspases in development, immunity, and apoptotic signal transduction: Lessons from knockout mice. Immunity 10:629–639.

Mayr, E. 1992. The idea of teleology. Journal of the History of Ideas 53:117–135.

McNally, K. L., N. S. Govind, P. E. Thome, and R. K. Trench. 1994. Small-subunit ribosomal DNA sequence analyses and a reconstruction of the inferred phylogeny among symbiotic dinoflagellates (Pyrrophyta). Journal of Phycology 30:316–329.

Mervis, J. 2003. Bye, bye biosphere 2. Science 302:2053.

Price, A. M. et al. 2008. A comparison of leaf and petal senescence in wallflower reveals common and distinct patterns of gene expression and physiology. Plant Physiology 147:1898–1912.

Reiss, J. O. 2007. Relative fitness, teleology, and the adaptive landscape. Evolutionary Biology 34:4–27.

Roberts, J. M., P. S. Davies, and L. M. Fixter. 1999. Symbiotic anemones can grow when starved: Nitrogen budget for *Anemonia viridis* in ammonium-supplemented seawater. Marine Biology 133:29–35.

Ross, H. 1995. The creator and the cosmos. NavPress, Colorado Springs, Colorado.

Roth, A. A. 2008. Science discovers God. Review and Herald Publishing, Hagerstown, Maryland.

Rowan, B. and D. A. Powers. 1991. A molecular genetic classification of zooxanthellae and the evolution of animal-algal symbioses. Science 251:1348–1351.

Terreros, M. T. 2003. Is all death a consequence of sin? Theological implications of alternative models. Journal of the Adventist Theological Society 14:150–175.

Wang, J. T. and A. E. Douglas. 1999. Essential amino acid synthesis and nitrogen recycling in an alga-invertebrate symbiosis. Marine Biology 135:219–222.

White, E. G. 1890. Patriarchs and Prophets. Review and Herald Publishing Association, Washington, DC.

White, E. G. 1946. Evangelism. Review and Herald Publishing Association, Washington, DC.

White, E. G. 1948. Testimonies for the church, volume 8. Pacific Press Publishing Association, Mountain View, California.

Wilson, D. S., and E. O. Wilson. 2008. Evolution "for the good of the group." American Scientist 96:380–389.

## Chapter Seven

# SEVENTH-DAY ADVENTIST FAITH AND ENVIRONMENTAL STEWARDSHIP[1]

## Floyd E. Hayes and William K. Hayes

In the last several decades, we have witnessed a global tsunami of growing concern for the natural environment. Although the environmental revolution has been embraced by a kaleidoscope of individuals representing virtually all socioeconomic classes, ethnic groups, nations, and religions, not all have jumped on the environmental bandwagon. Numerous studies reveal that individuals who identify themselves as political, social, and fiscal conservatives—including some among the evangelical bloc and so-called Christian right—are less concerned about environmental degradation than the general public (e.g., Guth et al. 1995; Schultz et al. 2000; McRight and Dunlap 2003; Allen et al. 2007; Sherkat and Ellison 2007; Konisky et al. 2008; Peterson and Liu 2008). Some—but certainly not all—conservatives perceive environmentalism as an ill-conceived threat to human freedom and prosperity. And although the vast majority of Christians—including Seventh-day Adventists—are genuinely concerned about human welfare, some neglect to link the quality of human life to the quality of the natural environment. As a consequence, Christian views of the natural environment and biological diversity are as varied as the cardinal points of the compass (for discussion of various perspectives, see Hall 1990; Land and Moore 1992; Oelschlaeger 1994; Van Dyke et al. 1996; Scharper 1998; Hessel and Ruether 2000; Bouma-Prediger 2001; Edwards and Worthing 2005; Berry 2006; Gottlieb 2006; Deane-Drummond 2008; Clements et al. 2013).

In this chapter, we will briefly summarize the diversity of Christian views about the environment, outline a biblical mandate for environmental

1. This paper is dedicated to the memory of Jimmy Ha, an assistant professor of religion and budding ecotheologian at Pacific Union College whose light flickered out much too soon—yet continues to shine in the lives of those whom he illuminated.

stewardship, and discuss distinct Adventist perspectives on the environment. We will then explore environmental education, research, and opportunities for student involvement in Adventist educational institutions, and conclude that the knowledge and understanding of environmental issues should permeate all levels of church membership.

## Christian Views of the Environment

Most Christians are moderate in their views of the environment, but there is a broad spectrum of perspectives (e.g., Guth et al. 1995; Shultz et al. 2000; Sherkat and Ellison 2007; Peterson and Liu 2008). At one extreme, some Christians view environmentalists and conservationists with suspicion—as radicals who conspire to achieve political control of our lives through regulation of environmental concerns. In an effort to distance themselves from environmental extremists, such Christians may appear indifferent or even hostile toward environmental stewardship.

Some Christians believe that God bequeathed us with an unlimited cornucopia of natural goods for our personal consumption and pleasure, and that limiting or denying access to such God-given blessings is a transgression of God's will for individual freedom. Those who embrace this materialistic perspective overlook the limited rate of renewal of natural resources and services imposed by natural processes, the currently unsustainable exploitation of natural resources for economic gain, and the fact that these blessings were not bestowed equally and fairly among all humans. Such materialism looks very much like idolatry.

Still others believe that no environmental problem exists which cannot be resolved by nature itself or, as a means of last resort, by human ingenuity and technology. However, Christians who cling to this assumption appear oblivious to the plight of those living in extreme poverty in regions where environmental degradation is already severe and the technology required to reverse it is lacking or unaffordable (e.g., Haiti; International Crisis Group 2009). Blind faith in technology can also be idolatry.

Some Christians despise the earth as a hostile, evil world that is merely a temporary home, which they are passing through and will soon escape from. This otherworldly view of future life fosters an attitude of apocalyptic apathy: Because the earth and everything on it will be destroyed when Jesus comes, why waste precious time and money trying to clean up or preserve what will be destroyed anyway? Nevertheless, such Christians continue to take care of their personal homes, vehicles, and other possessions, including their own bodies, all of which will also be destroyed.

Some Christians acknowledge that we should be concerned about the environment and biological diversity, but insist that the problems are exaggerated by scientists seeking more funding for their research and by environmentalists aspiring for political power. Suspicion of science occurs among some Christians who struggle to reconcile the conflict between the Scripture and science when it comes to the origin of life on the planet and the application of biotechnology (Ellison and Musick 1995; Morgan and Sternke 2007).

Finally, on the other side of the issue, some Christians have embraced an environmental ideology that holds that God not only demands that we care for His creation but also condemns those who ignorantly or wantonly destroy it. Such Christians may appear to be more concerned about the environment than about human welfare and rights. Environmental extremists, including some Christians, may do their cause more harm than good by repulsing those they seek to reach.

In one sense all Christians are environmentalists, at least when it comes to their personal environment. The staunchest environmental critics aspire to breathe clean air, drink pure water, eat uncontaminated food, and remove sewage and garbage from their homes. A few studies indicate that participation in organized religion often promotes private environmental actions but tends to negatively impact political environmental activism (Sherkat and Ellison 2007; c.f. Clements et al. 2013).

So how should Christians view the environment? In 1967, a provocative and widely cited essay, published in the prestigious journal *Science* by medieval historian Lynn White, blamed the triumph of Christianity as the root cause of the modern ecological crisis (1967). "By destroying pagan animism," White observed, "Christianity made it possible to exploit nature in a mood of indifference to the feelings of natural objects" (1967:1205). He concluded, "we shall continue to have a worsening ecologic crisis until we reject the Christian axiom that nature has no reason for existence save to serve man" (1967:1207). White's essay kindled introspection among Christian scholars, who subsequently scrutinized the Scriptures to reevaluate how Christians should relate to the environment. A new field of scholarship emerged from this study, now known as ecological theology or ecotheology (Santmire 1970).

Despite the disparity of views among Christian believers in general, a strong consensus emerged among ecotheologians that the Bible unequivocally mandates responsible environmental stewardship. Today, a growing number of Christians believe that we should be concerned about the access of *all* humans—not just ourselves and our closest kin, friends, or neighbors—to clean air, pure water, and uncontaminated food, and that we must proactively care for and preserve *all* of God's creation, both the living and nonliving components, not just for the benefit of humanity but because God cares for *all* of His creation and expects us to care as well. Christians who espouse this moderate but sincere view, which we believe better reflects the biblical position, will more likely win converts to their cause than those who promote extreme views.

## Biblical Mandate for Environmental Stewardship

So what does the Bible teach about environmental stewardship? The Bible clearly teaches that God is both Designer and Creator of all life forms as well as of the chemical and physical environments required to sustain life (Genesis 1–2; John 1:1–3; Colossians 1:16). In stark contrast with pantheistic pagan religions, which revere both inanimate and animate objects in nature as sacred, the Bible boldly declares that the earth and everything on it is not God but instead *belongs* to God, who is Ruler of His creation (Psalm 24:1; 1 Corinthians 10:26). The biogeochemical homeostasis of our planet provides evidence of God's intention for the earth "to be inhabited" (Isaiah 45:18).[2]

Although some Christians agree with White's (1967) "Christian axiom" that "nature has no reason for existence save to serve man," this view is not scriptural. God repeatedly pronounced as "good" His creative acts *before* humans were created (Genesis 1:4, 10, 12, 18, 21, 25, 31). Thus, every aspect of creation, both the living and nonliving, was bestowed with *intrinsic* value—the value of something independent of its value to anything else—rather than mere *utilitarian* value—the value something has as a means to another's ends, in this case for the benefit of humans (e.g., Cobb

2. All Scripture quotations, unless otherwise noted, are taken from the Holy Bible, New International Version®, NIV®. Copyright© 1973, 1978, 1984, 2011 by Biblica, Inc.™ Used by permission of Zondervan. All rights reserved worldwide. www.zondervan.com. The "NIV" and "New International Version" are trademarks registered in the United States Patent and Trademark Office by Biblica, Inc.™

1988). Psalm 104 eloquently praises the intrinsic value of some forms of biodiversity apart from human presence, including cedars, pines, storks, mountain goats, rock badgers, and lions, as well as the resources essential to sustain them. God's creation was never intended to be exploited or destroyed merely to satisfy human desires.

In the creation account, God gave man "dominion" (KJV) or permission to "rule" over all living things as well as permission to "subdue" the earth (Genesis 1:26, 28). Was this dominion a license to kill, or a mandate for stewardship? Although the belief by many Christians in a God-given right to dominate all other forms of life deserves some blame for the destruction of biodiversity (e.g., White 1967; Passmore 1974; Orr 2005; see excellent reviews in Berry 2006), the dominion was given before sin entered the planet (Genesis 3), before skins were needed for clothing (Genesis 3:21), and long before humans were allowed to kill animals for food (Genesis 9:3). The Hebrew word for "dominion," *radah,* invokes the rule of a king, but God-associated royal rulership with benevolence toward the weak and needy (Psalm 72:8–14). God specifically prohibited rulers from accumulating horses, wives, silver, or gold (Deuteronomy 17:16–17). The actual meaning of *dominion* thus contrasts sharply with the indifference and exploitation—explicitly condemned in Ezekiel 34:2–4—that secular critics often ascribe to this term. Jesus described the ideal ruler: "whoever wants to become great among you must be your servant, and whoever wants to be first must be your slave" (Matthew 20:26–27). Therefore the dominion given to humankind was clearly a mandate for responsible stewardship of the earth.

After being placed in the Garden of Eden, Adam was commanded "to dress it and keep it" (KJV) or "to work it and take care of it" (Genesis 2:15), revealing God's intention for us to maintain and protect His creation. This instruction further clarifies the meaning of "dominion" in Genesis 1:28. The word *dress* (Hebrew *abad*) means "to work or serve," and the word *keep* (Hebrew *shamar*) means "to exercise great care over." To avoid the degradation of farm land from overuse, God instructed that the land be allowed to lie fallow every seventh year (Leviticus 25:2–7). Often, God found it necessary to remind the Hebrews of this mandate: "The land is mine and you are but aliens and my tenants. Throughout the country that you hold as a possession, you must provide for the redemption of the land" (Leviticus 25:23–24; see also Ezekiel 34:17–18 and Jeremiah 2:7).

The sacred Scriptures repeatedly remind us of our moral obligation to treat animals humanely by providing them with sufficient rest and food (e.g., Exodus 23:5, 12; Deuteronomy 25:4); rescuing them from harm (Matthew 12:11); and never torturing them (Numbers 22:23–33). Although some environmentally indifferent Christians question the wisdom of the U.S. Endangered Species Act, the command for Noah to bring with him living creatures into the ark—"to keep them alive" (Genesis 6:19)—might actually be considered the first legislation of its kind. Indeed, God provides for the needs of all creatures, not just humans (e.g., Job 38:19–41; Psalms 36:6; 104:27–28; 147:9; Jonah 4:11; Matthew 6:26). Should we be any less benevolent?

In Revelation, environmental disasters of an unprecedented magnitude are portended by the seven plagues predicted to occur just before Jesus returns: (1) "ugly and painful sores"; (2) the sea and (3) rivers becoming blood; (4) the sun scorching men with fire; (5) darkness upon the seat of the beast; (6) the great Euphrates River drying up; and (7) thunder, lightning, and hail, plus an earthquake (Revelation 16). We can only speculate what the plagues refer to, but we are unequivocally informed that God will be "destroying those who destroy the earth" (Revelation 11:18).

Rightfully understood, the teachings of the Bible cannot be blamed as the root cause of modern environmental problems. Although Christendom (a society), rather than Christianity (a religion), certainly deserves its share of blame, those who persist in blaming Christians should contemplate the environmental degradation that occurred in Communist and other non-Christian countries. As examples of the latter, the long-term scars resulting from deforestation, overgrazing, erosion, and overhunting in ancient civilizations that viewed nature as sacred can still be observed in modern landscapes in regions as diverse as India and China (e.g., Tuan 1970; Novak 1993), New Mexico, Central America, and many Pacific islands (e.g., Diamond 1994). The Bible identifies the root cause of environmental degradation as sin—transgressing the moral and natural laws of God (Isaiah 24:5; Hosea 4:1–3)—which all humans manifest (Romans 3:23), as greed, pride, carelessness, and ignorance (Wright 1970).

Among God's creations on this planet, will humans alone be redeemed? Most Christians believe that only humans who believe are promised eternal life (John 3:16), but various ecotheologians have proffered biblical evidence that Jesus died to save the world—not just humans—from the effects of sin and suffering (e.g., John 3:16–17). In this view, our entire planet will one day be redeemed through cleansing (2 Peter 3:10); restoration (e.g., Isaiah 11:1–9; 65:17–23; Ezekiel 36:33–35; Romans 8:19–23; Revelation 21:1, 5) rather than destruction will take place; and sin will ultimately be banished from the universe (Nahum 1:9; Revelation 21:4).

Today many environmental and conservation organizations are dedicated to preserving natural resources. Most of these organizations were founded and remain governed by nonreligious people who care deeply about nature. While these organizations often include Christians and people of other faiths as members, unfortunately some Christians have essentially abandoned the care of God's creation to those who deny the Creator—despite the divine mandate for stewardship of our planet's resources.

Although White unfairly blamed Christianity for environmental problems, he conceded that "the remedy must also be essentially religious" (1967). Christianity and other faiths may play a crucial role in engaging environmental problems, for two reasons. First, nearly 90% of the world's 6.8 billion people are religious adherents; thus, the weight of the faith community can tip the scales in support of pro-environment programs. Secular organizations increasingly recognize this; as a result, they have initiated outreach programs aimed at identifying common ground and building cooperation between science and religion (e.g., Awoyemi 2008; Peterson and Liu 2008; Dudley et al. 2009; Woodhams 2009). Second, virtually all credible ideas for addressing environmental problems require some sacrifice (Hardin 1968), and religion is the most potent force that can effectively inspire followers to sacrifice for the common good. Although sociobiologists have demonstrated sustainable benefits for cooperative behavior, including altruism (the loss of one's own benefits for the sake of another individual), "cheaters" within a cooperative system can benefit in ways that destabilize the system (Gächter and Herrmann 2009). Religious values may reinforce the need for self-sacrifice that evolutionary theory, from a selfish gene or individual perspective, denies.

## Distinct Seventh-day Adventist Perspectives on the Environment

The Seventh-day Adventist Church does not endorse any unique position on environmental stewardship, but our theological views offer some distinctive perspectives. The Adventist commitment to observe the Fourth

Commandment—to remember the Sabbath day, keep it holy, and refrain from work (Exodus 20:8–11)—perpetually reminds us of God's creation and our moral obligation to care for it. During the Sabbath, many Adventists enjoy exploring the outdoors and learning about God's creation, thus nurturing an intimate relationship with the Creator and other created beings. The widespread degradation of the environment readily visible when exploring the outdoors is a sad reminder of the consequences of disobeying God's moral and natural laws. Adventists believe that sin will ultimately be banished from the universe (Nahum 1:9; Revelation 21:4) and that the planet will one day be restored to its original perfection (Revelation 21:1).

Adventists regard the human body as "a temple of the Holy Spirit" (1 Corinthians 6:19) and strive to balance the physical, mental, and spiritual aspects of human nature through conformity with God's moral and natural laws. The prolific writings of Ellen White encouraged Adventists to live simply in the rural countryside (1946); to develop the mind, character, and personality through education (1903; 1977); and to live a healthy lifestyle (1905; 1938). Many Adventists aspire to live the ideal Adventist lifestyle in a rural area, breathing fresh air, engaging frequently in vigorous exercise, consuming a balanced diet of natural foods, drinking wholesome beverages, and worshipping both individually and corporately.

Living the ideal Adventist lifestyle reduces an individual's ecological footprint. To give an example, many Adventists are vegetarians, a lifestyle choice that contributes to their greater longevity compared with that of the general population (Fraser 2003). Significantly, vegetarianism also benefits the environment. A recent study by Loma Linda University researchers calculated that, for the combined differential production of 11 food items for which consumption differed between Seventh-day Adventist vegetarians and nonvegetarians in California, the nonvegetarian diet required 2.9 times more water, 2.5 times more primary energy, 13 times more fertilizer, and 1.4 times more pesticides than did the vegetarian diet (Marlow et al. 2009).

The Adventist church has issued several declarations about the need to exercise environmental stewardship. These official statements were approved by vote in 1992, 1995, and 1996 (see Appendix C). The first statement emphasized Adventist beliefs in a Creator God, the Sabbath as a memorial of God's creative act, and the environmental degradation that resulted from breaking the original order of creation. Recognizing the interrelatedness of environmental degradation and quality of life, church leaders called for sustainable development of resources while meeting human needs.

The second statement acknowledged the megalomaniacal destruction of Earth's resources, largely due to human selfishness and the egocentric overutilization of resources, and recognized that our failure to rule the natural environment in a faithful and fruitful way has led to widespread human suffering. Adventists were urged to lead a simple, wholesome lifestyle, show respect for creation, and exercise restraint in the use of the world's resources. The third statement, which emerged during an Annual Council session held in Costa Rica, emphasized the same points as the second statement and commended the government and people of Costa Rica for their support of a comprehensive policy of sustainable development in harmony with nature.

In 2008, Jan Paulsen, at that time the General Conference President, issued an informal but clear mandate for increased discourse on environmental stewardship (2008). He reminded us that the dominion God extended to humanity was an act of trust, a special responsibility to administer wisely the resources He has generously bestowed upon us.

Although Adventist leadership has voiced clear concern for environmental stewardship, no institution, department, or appointed leader has been tasked with meeting this important need. In August 2009, the Loma Linda University board approved the creation of a new Center for Biodiversity and Conservation Studies in an effort to fill this void.

## Seventh-day Adventist Environmental Education

The Bible clearly conveys our need to study and learn from nature. "But ask the animals, and they will teach you, or the birds of the air, and they will tell you; or speak to the earth, and it will teach you, or let the fish of the sea inform you" (Job 12:7–8). Object lessons from nature abound in Holy Writ, and Jesus Himself made frequent reference to these. Ellen White likewise emphasized the importance of nature study: "God has surrounded us with nature's beautiful scenery to attract and interest the mind. It is His design that we should associate the glories of nature with His character. If we faithfully study the book of nature, we shall find it a fruitful source for contemplating the infinite love and power of God" (1952:144). "Tell your children about the miracle-working power of God. As they study the great lesson book of nature, God will impress their minds" (1954:57). "God's great book of nature is open for us to study, and from it we are to gain more exalted ideas of His greatness and unexcelled love and glory" (White 1958:26).

Reflecting on our own childhood experiences, we enthusiastically advocate the approach our parents used in nurturing our interest in nature. As a family, we enjoyed frequent outdoor picnics, nature hikes, and visits to nature centers, zoos, and museums, especially on Sabbath afternoons. We also enjoyed camping on a regular basis. Our growing fascination with nature sheltered us during our teenage years from the many temptations associated with peer pressure. Rather than hanging out with peers of sometimes questionable influence, we were more content to wander the forest behind our home in search of frogs and snakes and to climb onto the roof of our home to watch migrating birds. Our parents tolerated a small menagerie of amphibians and reptiles (the covertly acquired venomous snakes were another matter). Our local church provided occasional nature-oriented programs, particularly through the Pathfinder clubs in which we participated.

Environmental education likewise occurs at some level in virtually all Adventist institutions of learning, where nature, God's "second book," has traditionally been upheld. Some efforts by elementary and secondary schools, as well as local churches, have had a major impact on local communities. To cite a stellar example, Lomino described a project with 7th and 8th grade students who studied the ecology of Wolftever Creek, a notoriously polluted stream flowing through Collegedale, Tennessee (1999). The students developed a museum, produced publications and a video, formed a legal nonprofit corporation, raised funds, and successfully lobbied the local government to help restore the creek and protect it from further degradation.

Those aspiring to become environmental scientists will need to make important decisions about their career paths. Choosing a suitable major is an important step. Traditional science majors such as biology, chemistry, and geology generally provide a good launching pad for environmental careers. An environmental science or environmental studies major is more interdisciplinary in scope but typically provides less training in the hard sciences. Although the job market for environmental scientists continues to expand, earning a graduate degree will certainly make one more competitive when it comes to the more desired and higher-paying jobs.

Most Adventist colleges and universities offer an introductory course on the environment. However, only a few North American institutions offer undergraduate degrees in environmental science or environmental studies. These include Canadian University College, Loma Linda University, Pacific Union College, and Walla Walla University.

Post-baccalaureate students who wish to continue their environmental education in a Seventh-day Adventist university in North America can obtain relevant graduate degrees at three tertiary institutions. Andrews University and Walla Walla University offer master's degrees in biology that provide environmental coursework and have several faculty actively investigating environmental issues with graduate and undergraduate students. Loma Linda University (LLU) provides both MS and PhD degrees in biology and geology, both of which offer strong emphases on the environment. Another program at LLU, the Department of Environmental and Occupational Health in the School of Public Health, offers several graduate degrees that take a human-focused approach to environmental issues.

Students seeking careers in environmental science should consider nontraditional approaches to their education that broaden their training. Conventional undergraduate degrees in the sciences provide a strong background, but these programs commonly lack training in the human sciences. Graduate programs also tend to be relatively narrow, primarily emphasizing the development of technical skills associated with research. As the workforce has become increasingly interdisciplinary, global, and collaborative, professional environmental scientists must often rely on a diverse set of skills that includes problem solving and evaluation, teamwork, conflict resolution and negotiation, planning, communication, organization, management, and leadership (Pérez 2005; Kroll 2007). Other valuable knowledge and skills include public speaking and communication, environmental law and ethics, policy analysis, marketing and social psychology, and economics and fundraising (Pérez 2005), which means students should consider coursework in the social sciences (Fisher et al. 2009).

Although theory is important, training in environmental science must also include practical experiences. Environmental scientists need to develop problem-solving skills and apply them in real-world situations (Kainer et al. 2006). Further, students should be exposed as much as possible to outdoor inquiry-based learning, which inspires fascination and respect for the environment, while fostering the development of naturalistic intelligence

(Hayes 2009). Learning can also begin early; for example, students given an opportunity to participate in original scientific research while in high school are more likely to enter a career in science (Roberts and Wassersug 2009). (If your professors fail to include a significant field—or other practical—component in relevant courses, suggest that they consider making changes to ensure hands-on learning.)

## Importance of Environmental Research

Some Christians, including Seventh-day Adventists, tend to disparage studies of obscure microorganisms, plants, animals, and ecosystems that have no obvious relevance to human health. However, many examples demonstrate the importance of learning about our planet's fellow inhabitants. One can seldom predict how significant a seemingly trivial discovery may become!

As one example, basic research into *Thermus aquaticus,* an obscure, thermophilic bacterium that thrives in the hot springs of Yellowstone National Park, ushered in a new era in molecular biology and modern medicine. An enzyme isolated from this organism, relied on today for amplifying tiny bits of DNA, became *Science* magazine's first Molecule of the Year in 1989, and later earned Dr. Kary Mullis a Nobel Prize in 1993 for refining the amplification process that is a cornerstone of modern molecular biology. Unfortunately, the original discovery of the thermophilic bacterium by Thomas Brock, an Indiana University professor, and his graduate student, Hudson Freeze, is seldom recognized (Brock and Freeze 1969). Where would we be today if they had not conducted the basic exploratory studies of this nondescript bacterium?

As another example, our planet is rapidly being transformed by the microbes, plants, and animals that we have transplanted from one place to another, sometimes deliberately and other times unwittingly. Consider: Introduced fungi and insects wipe out our forests and devastate our crops. Introduced viruses (e.g., West Nile) kill reptiles, birds, and even humans in places where the diseases they inflict never existed before. Introduced freshwater mollusks damage boats, harbors, dams, water-treatment plants, and power plants. Introduced mosquitoes, snakes, rodents, and cats have exterminated entire populations of lizards and birds on islands. The consequences of invasive species are staggering, not only for ecosystems but also to commerce. In the United States alone, invasive species inflict damage and control costs that exceed $138 billion annually (Pimentel et al. 2005). Could much of this have been prevented or more quickly ameliorated by basic research? Absolutely.

In reality, when we care for the fragile ecosystems around us, we truly are taking care of ourselves. The bewildering complexity and interconnectedness of even the simplest ecosystems render them highly vulnerable to disturbance. Even mild disruption of natural processes can lead to eventual ecosystem collapse. Most of us take for granted the abundant ecosystem services that we daily depend upon. These include provision of food and water; pollination of native and agricultural plants; cycling of nutrients; moderation of extreme weather, including flood and drought mitigation; protection against erosion; regulation of plant pests and human disease organisms; decomposition and detoxification of wastes; purification of air and water; and maintenance of biodiversity. These services, provided to us for free, have been valued globally at $33 trillion per annum, which at the time of the study exceeded the entire human exchange economy (Costanza et al. 1997). Without these services, which we are rapidly degrading and which cannot be readily replaced, our quality of life would be fundamentally diminished.

Clearly, given the biblical and denominational mandates, we must be active participants in the stewardship of our planet. We should be in the forefront of the cause, committed to learning more about and helping to save our planet's cohabitants and the ecosystems they require.

In reality, many Adventist scientists are indeed engaged in this endeavor, although much of their work remains unknown to most church members. The most visible environmental research in the church takes place at its North American tertiary campuses. Many of the faculty who publish relevant research in professional journals are listed in Appendix D (updated as of January 2014); visit their individual or departmental websites to learn about their specific work. Other church members, scattered among secular universities and at government and nongovernment agencies, similarly enjoy productive research careers.

The environmental arena can bring together two often-polarized enterprises—science and religion—for a common good. As pointed out by Harvard biologist Edward O. Wilson, "Science and religion are two of the most potent forces on Earth and they should come together to save the Creation" (Cromie 2006). Some perceive that Adventist biologists and geologists face religious bias, and therefore are unable to publish in legitimate scientific venues. Fortunately, most Adventist scientists have not experienced such bias, as faculty and students at our Adventist colleges and universities have an excellent track record for their contributions to science. This should be no surprise; a large minority of North American university professors are religious, including nearly 40% of biologists and psychologists—the disciplines with the highest proportion of professed atheists or agnostics (Gross and Simmons 2009). By participating in research, students at our institutions gain hands-on experience with cutting-edge technology, develop critical-thinking and communication skills, and greatly enrich their learning experience.

## Opportunities for Student Involvement

Students should realize that environmental problems are not caused by society, but instead are caused by individuals; as a consequence, resolving environmental problems must begin with the individual (Ness 1991). Student opportunities for involvement abound. Students who engage environmental issues can profoundly influence the attitudes of their family, peers, academic institutions, local churches, and, ultimately, their denominations. Here, we suggest specific activities that can be implemented on a high-school, college, or university campus. Many of these may require a faculty or department sponsor. Most important, we encourage students to avoid politicizing environmental issues, which tends to be divisive, and focus instead on issues of common concern.

1. Organize or participate in an environmental club. Strength accrues with numbers. If one or more such clubs already exist (e.g., within the biology department), consider an alternative club and theme that appeals to a different interest group (e.g., Musicians for the Environment). If possible, organize a speaker program for club members or for the campus at large. The SEEDS program at Oakwood University (www.oakwood.edu/seeds/index.html) serves as an excellent model for the diverse range of activities it sponsors.
2. Organize or participate in a recycling program. These programs tend to be highly visible and can potentially generate income. Special collection bins with an attractive appearance, including

a catchy slogan or logo, will draw further attention to your cause. Permission will be needed to distribute these bins. If your campus already has a program in place, consider ways to improve it. Local businesses or communities may also benefit from a more visible recycling program, so consider extending your program to the off-campus community.

3. Write for your school or community paper. You can highlight local issues or the activities of specific individuals, or simply share general concepts or experiences.
4. Work with a faculty sponsor to design and conduct an environmental study for your senior or honors research. Projects may range from ecological studies to surveys of student attitudes and, when done well, may result in publication in a professional journal (e.g., Shultz et al. 2000; Peterson and Liu 2008).
5. Request that occasional worships and sermons focus on environmental issues. Consider on-campus speakers (e.g., from the biology department), off-campus authorities, fellow students, or volunteer yourself. You can supply relevant information to potential speakers, including your campus chaplain or local church pastor.
6. Organize or participate in a community project that draws attention to environmental issues. Examples include a community cleanup, planting trees, carpooling, building a nature trail, plant or animal surveys, a fund-raising project for a specific program, and a recycling drive. Be creative in generating ideas. Although higher-profile projects may draw more attention to your cause, mere participation will be meaningful to those who help out.
7. Participate in programs that educate the public about environmental issues. Consider arranging or giving a talk to an elementary or high-school class, a church group, a local business group, a local nature organization, or residents of a retirement community. Remember: Illustrated talks always work better!
8. Volunteer to work at or seek an internship with an environmental group. ADRA (Adventist Disaster and Relief Agency) engages environmental issues to some extent, and many opportunities exist in the broader community. The Internet is a good place to search for opportunities. If you are clever, you just might find yourself gaining valuable experience in an exotic location!

9. Reduce your personal ecological footprint at home, at work, and at play. Think in terms of energy consumption (e.g., lighting; clothes dryer, television, and other appliance use; room temperature control; food preparation); water usage (e.g., shower use, lawn watering, dishwashing, car washing); material consumption (e.g., buying used furniture and vehicles, reusing shopping bags, avoiding drinks in plastic bottles); transportation (e.g., walking, biking, or carpooling when possible); and waste disposal (e.g., reduce, reuse, recycle).

## Conclusions

Careful scholarship demonstrates a clear biblical call for environmental stewardship. Influenced by Ellen White's writings, Adventists have historically emphasized the study of nature, God's "second book." However, in spite of official statements released by the church endorsing a simple lifestyle, sustainable development, and environmental sensitivity, some Seventh-day Adventists remain skeptical of environmental concerns.

Fortunately, many educators within the church have sought to increase both discourse and action. Our colleges and universities, in particular, have provided leadership that may galvanize change. We advocate increased curricular emphasis on environmental issues and, when possible, active research programs involving students: our future leaders. Our hope is that a new generation of environmentally sensitive Adventists will energize the church and usher in an exciting new era of environmental consciousness, stewardship, and witness.

## Literature Cited

Allen, R. S., E. Castano, and P. D. Allen. 2007. Conservatism and concern for the environment. Quarterly Journal of Ideology 30(3/4):1–25.

Awoyemi, S. M. 2008. The role of religion in the HIV/AIDS intervention in Africa: A possible model for conservation biology. Conservation Biology 22:811–813.

Berry, R. J. (ed.). 2006. Environmental stewardship: Critical perspectives—past and present. T & T Clark, London, United Kingdom.

Bouma-Prediger, S. 2001. For the beauty of the earth: A Christian vision for creation care. Baker Academic, Grand Rapids, Michigan.

Brock, T. D., and H. Freeze. 1969. *Thermus aquaticus*, a nonsporulating extreme thermophile. Journal of Bacteriology 98:289–297.

Clements, J. M., A. M. McCright, and C. Xiao. 2013. Green Christians? An empirical examination of environmental concern within the U.S. general public. Organization & Environment. DOI 10.1177/1086026613495475.

Cobb, J. B., Jr. 1988. A Christian view of biodiversity. Pp. 481–485 in Biodiversity (E. O. Wilson and F. M. Peter, eds). National Academy Press, Washington, DC.

Costanza, R. et al. 1997. The value of the world's ecosystem services and natural capital. Nature 387:253–260.

Cromie, W. J. 2006. Naturalist E. O. Wilson is optimistic. Harvard Gazette, June 15, 2006.

Deane-Drummond, C. 2008. Eco-Theology. Saint Mary's Press, Winona, Minnesota.

Diamond, J. M. 1994. Ecological collapses of ancient civilizations: The golden age that never was. Bulletin of the American Academy of Arts and Sciences 47(5):37–59.

Dudley, N., L. Higgins-Zogib, and S. Mansourian. 2009. The links between protected areas, faiths, and sacred natural sites. Conservation Biology 23:568–577.

Edwards, D., and M. W. Worthing (eds.). 2005. Biodiversity and ecology: An interdisciplinary challenge. ATF Press, Adelaide.

Ellison, C. G., and M. A. Musick. 1995. Conservative Protestantism and public opinion toward science. Review of Religious Research 36:245–262.

Fisher, B., A. Balmford, R. E. Green, and R. Trevelyan. 2009. Conservation science training: The need for an extra dimension. Oryx 43:361–363.

Fraser, G. E. 2003. Diet, life expectancy, and chronic disease: Studies of Seventh-day Adventists and other vegetarians. Oxford University Press, New York.

Gächter, S., and B. Herrmann. 2009. Reciprocity, culture and human cooperation: Previous insights and a new cross-cultural experiment. Philosophical Transactions of the Royal Society B 364:791–806.

Gottlieb, R. S. 2006. A greener faith: Religious environmentalism and our planet's future. Oxford University Press, Oxford, United Kingdom.

Gross, N., and S. Simmons. 2009. The religiosity of American college and university professors. Sociological Analysis. DOI 10.1093/socrel/srp026.

Guth, J. L., J. C. Green, L. A. Kellstedt, and C. E. Smidt. 1995. Faith and the environment: Religious beliefs and attitudes on environmental policy. American Journal of Political Science 39:364–382.

Hall, D. J. 1990. The steward: A biblical symbol come of age. Eerdmans, Grand Rapids, Michigan.

Hardin, G. 1968. The tragedy of the commons. Science 162:1243–1248.

Hayes, M. A. 2009. Into the field: Naturalistic education and the future of conservation. Conservation Biology 23:1075–1079.

Hessel, D. T., and R. R. Ruether (eds.). 2000. Christianity and ecology. Harvard University Center for the Study of World Religions, Cambridge, Massachusetts.

International Crisis Group. 2009. Haiti: Saving the environment, preventing instability and conflict. Crisis Group Latin America and Caribbean Briefing no. 20, 28 April 2009. Brussels, Belgium.

Kainer, K. A. et al. 2006. A graduate education framework for tropical conservation and development. Conservation Biology 20:3–13.

Konisky, D. M., J. Milyo, and L. E. Richardson, Jr. 2008. Environmental policy attitudes: Issues, geographic scale, and political trust. Social Science Quarterly 89:1066–1085.

Kroll, A. J. 2007. Integrating professional skills in wildlife student education. Journal of Wildlife Management 71:226–230.

Land, R. D., and L. Moore. 1992. The earth is the Lord's: Christians and the environment. Broadman Press, Nashville, Tennessee.

Lomino, J. A. 1999. Mission environment: Using the world as a lesson book. Journal of Adventist Education 61(4):16–20.

Marlow, H. J., W. K. Hayes, S. Soret, R. L. Carter, E. R. Schwab, and J. Sabaté. 2009. Diet and the environment: Does what you eat matter? American Journal of Clinical Nutrition 89: 1699S–1703S.

McCright, A. M., and R. E. Dunlap. 2003. Defeating Kyoto: The conservative movement's impact on U.S. climate change policy. Social Problems 50:348–373.

Morgan, K. H., and E. A. Sternke. 2007. The effects of religiosity on attitudes towards science and biomedical research: A structural equation model analysis. Paper presented at the annual meeting of the American Sociological Association, New York. Available at www.allacademic.com/meta/p183885_index.html. Accessed 8 May 2010.

Ness, B. 1991. Environmental education: Teaching stewardship to college students. Journal of Adventist Education 53 (3):32–36.

Novak, P. 1993. Tao how? Asian religions and the problem of environmental degradation. ReVision 16:77–82.

Oelschlaeger, M. 1994. Caring for creation: An ecumenical approach to the environmental Crisis. Yale University Press, New Haven, Connecticut.

Orr, D. W. 2005. Armageddon versus extinction. Conservation Biology 19:290–292.

Passmore, J. A. 1974. Man's responsibility for nature: Ecological problems and western traditions. Scribner Sons, New York.

Paulsen, J. 2008. Freedom to care. Adventist World 4(7):8–10.

Pérez, H. E. 2005. What students can do to improve graduate education in conservation biology. Conservation Biology 19:2033–2035.

Peterson, M. N., and J. Liu. 2008. Impacts of religion on environmental worldviews: The Teton Valley case. Society and Natural Resources 21:704–718.

Pimentel, D., R. Zuniga, and D. Morrison. 2005. Update on the environmental and economic costs associated with alien-invasive species in the United States. Ecological Economics 52:273–288.

Roberts, L. F., and R. J. Wassersug. 2009. Does doing scientific research in high school correlate with students staying in science? A half-century retrospective study. Research in Science Education 39:251–256.

Santmire, H. P. 1970. Brother earth: Nature, God, and ecology in time of crisis. Thomas Nelson, New York.

Scharper, S. B. 1998. Redeeming the time: A political theology of the environment. Continuum International Publishing Group, London, United Kingdom.

Schultz, P. W., L. Zelezny, and N. J. Dalrymple. 2000. A multinational perspective on the relation between Judeo-Christian religious beliefs and attitudes of environmental concern. Environment and Behavior 32:576–591.

Sherkat, D. E., and C. G. Ellison. 2007. Structuring the religion-environment connection: Identifying religious influences on environmental concern and activism. Journal for the Scientific Study of Religion 46:71–85.

Tuan, Y. 1970. Our treatment of the environment in ideal and actuality. American Scientist 58:244–249.

Van Dyke, F., D. C. Mahan, J. K. Sheldon, and R. H. Brand. 1996. Redeeming creation: The biblical basis for environmental stewardship. InterVarsity Press, Downers Grove, Illinois.

White, A. L. 1982. Ellen G. White: The later Elmshaven years. Vol. 6. 1905–1915. Review and Herald Publishing Association, Takoma Park, Maryland.

White, E. G. 1903. Education. Pacific Press Publishing Association, Mountain View, California.

White, E. G. 1905. The ministry of healing. Pacific Press Publishing Association, Mountain View, California.

White, E. G. 1909. Advantages of the Angwin property. Pacific Union Recorder, September 23.

White, E. G. 1938. Counsels on diet and foods. Review and Herald Publishing Association, Takoma Park, Maryland.

White, E. G. 1946. Country living: An aid to moral and social security. Review and Herald Publishing Association, Takoma Park, Maryland.

White, E. G. 1952. The Adventist home. Southern Publishing Association, Nashville, Tennessee.

White, E. G. 1954. Child guidance. Southern Publishing Association, Nashville, Tennessee.

White, E. G. 1958. The faith I live by. Review and Herald Publishing Association, Takoma Park, Maryland.

White, E. G. 1977. Mind, character, and personality. 2 vols. Southern Publishing Association, Nashville, Tennessee.

White, L., Jr. 1967. The historical roots of our ecologic crisis. Science 155:1203–1207.

Woodhams, D. C. 2009. Converting the religious: Putting amphibian conservation in context. Bioscience 59:463–464.

Wright, R. T. 1970. Responsibility for the ecological crisis. Bioscience 20:851–853.

## Chapter Eight

# CREATIONISM, DARWINISM, AND MERE SCIENCE

**Earl M. J. Aagaard**

As a young biology teacher at Pacific Union College, I determined to teach both the pros and cons of Darwinian evolutionary theory. I believed students would assume my commitment to Adventist faith, including the Genesis account of Creation, as I had assumed the same about my own professors. I was horrified one day when a colleague in the religion department told me that a student had expressed surprise that I was a traditional creationist. He said that I had devoted a lot of time to Darwinism and evolution, while never explicitly sharing my own beliefs. That very day I began to rewrite the relevant portions of my lecture notes. Never again did I discuss the Darwinian view without engaging its strengths and weaknesses, as well as drawing an explicit contrast between it and my own view.

This experience showed me the importance of integrating my Adventist beliefs into how I study and teach biology. This book has attempted to accomplish this integration across a wide range of disciplines, from genomics to ecology. In this chapter, I will draw from these essays and from other sources to affirm this importance and to urge you, the reader, to think carefully about the relationship between your beliefs and science in general. Specifically, I hope to convince you of the truth of the following propositions:

1. When we discuss contentious issues, it is essential for all participants to define terms carefully and use them consistently.
2. Science is not a monolithic entity but includes at least two rather different enterprises. Accepting some scientific interpretations while rejecting others is not necessarily irrational or intellectually dishonest.
3. We scientists are human beings, with the same tendencies and weaknesses as the rest of humanity. We each have a worldview, a set of foundational assumptions that directs us in what we

choose to study, what we recognize as data, and especially what interpretation we come up with to explain the evidence.

4. There are two major worldviews (theism and materialism[1]) in the Western world, and at times they resemble competing religions. Perhaps scientists could get along together, regardless of worldview differences, if they would do their scientific work within the paradigm currently referred to as intelligent design.
5. Finally, Christians must continue to embrace the biblical worldview, and with it the creationist account of origins as described in Genesis—or they risk losing the logical foundation for Christian faith.

## Definitions and Why They Matter

Making distinctions is a sign of careful thinking, and carefully defining our terms is the first step. As noted above, the precise definitions of the words we use are crucial, particularly when they are used in debate. Phillip Johnson discussed this in his influential book *Darwin on Trial* (1991). He observed that having control over the definitions often means winning the argument.

Let us illustrate with important terms from the present book. In chapter 1, Thomas Goodwin describes *science* as "a way to gain empirically testable knowledge about nature." This is a traditional definition, and most people think of "testing" as something that occurs only in a laboratory under controlled conditions. This is a misunderstanding, because scientists "test" ideas in different ways, but we need to be aware of it if we wish to foster clear thinking about these issues. If we accept for the moment this popular definition, then it does not cover everything that scientists do, much of which involves collecting data and drawing inferences that cannot be definitively tested experimentally. For example, this traditional definition breaks down when we ask, Where did the first living thing come from? We are unable to definitively test, by experiment, our theories about the origin of life. If a group of scientists assembled the appropriate chemicals and

1. By *materialism* (used here synonymously with *naturalism*), I mean the philosophy that rejects all spiritual, supernatural, or teleological explanations *a priori,* holding that matter and energy are sufficient causes to explain everything that exists—including our minds (Hirsch et al. 2002), although the origin of both matter and energy are left a mystery.

designed a system that produced a living organism from nonliving materials, what further experiment could confirm that this is (or is not) how life actually came about in the beginning? Furthermore, what would the original experiment actually show us about how a living cell might have originated, since the method used appears to lend more support to intelligent design than to random events.

Another term with multiple definitions is *evolution,* as Leonard Brand clearly elucidates with his discussion of microevolution, macroevolution, and megaevolution (chapter 4). In both popular and technical media, the term may mean something as noncontroversial as "change over time"—a process easily observed and beyond reasonable dispute. However, *evolution* is also used to refer to a totally hypothetical scenario that begins with the spontaneous generation of a cell with its DNA code and continues with its elaboration, by unguided processes such as mutation and natural selection over many millions of years, to craft the rich diversity and complexity of all subsequent life. The latter definition is unsupported experimentally, but it is currently the only interpretation of life's history presented in our textbooks, because it is the only viable option given the worldview of materialism.

*Environmentalist* is also a term that must be carefully defined. I feel justified in rejecting the label if it identifies me with the Earth Liberation Front, Greenpeace, or even perhaps the Sierra Club. Alternatively, if it means careful stewardship of God's creation for the support and enjoyment of humankind, then it is both noncontroversial for—and properly supported by—Christians. In their discussion of environmental concerns (chapter 7), William and Floyd Hayes carefully define several contentious terms such as *dominion, Christendom,* and *Christianity,* but their argument would be stronger if they clearly defined other important words, such as *overutilization, degradation,* and *exploited.*

Let us now return to the definition of *science.* Over the last four decades, there has been a distinct evolution in how *science* is defined. When I was in college, my zoology textbook defined science as follows:

> Science…is exact knowledge or tested and verified human experience.… The raw materials of science are **facts,** the real state of things.… Thus the scientific method accepts no knowledge as completely fixed or infallible but constantly seeks added evidence to test and to formulate basic principles of nature. (Storer and Usinger 1965:3; emphasis in original)

I always understood this to be the ideal for which working scientists should strive, especially in the experimental areas, although I now suspect the definition had an ideological goal: to get the public to be less critical of and more likely to accept the conclusions of science.

Much later, I was struck by the significantly different view of science presented in the general biology text from which I taught. After extensive discussion of "unifying themes that apply specifically to the study of life" ending with evolution as the "core theme" and "unifying thread" of biology, the author provides the following description of science:

> [W]e now examine some general features of science as a process. Like life, science is better understood by observing it than by trying to create a precise definition.... Science is a way of knowing.... At the heart of science are people asking questions about nature and believing that those questions are answerable.... A process known as the scientific method outlines a series of steps for answering questions, but few scientists adhere rigidly to this prescription.... Like other intellectual activities, the best science is a process of minds that are creative, intuitive, imaginative, and social. *Perhaps science is distinguished by its conviction that natural phenomena, including the processes of life, have* ***natural*** *causes*—and by its obsession with evidence. (Campbell et al. 1999:13–14; emphasis added)

Note how the textbook view of science has changed in 34 years: from a process dealing with "facts" to a "way of knowing" that looks for "natural causes." With the earlier definition of *science,* a transcendent Designer is an option if the facts of nature can most logically be interpreted in that way. The more recent definition of *science,* however, rules out a Designer before science even begins: only "natural causes" are allowed. Phillip Johnson warned about this ongoing process of change in the definition of *science:* away from one involving specific procedures following shared rules to find explanations limited only by their logical connections to the evidence—and toward one that is effectively applied materialist philosophy (1998).

This move to equate science with materialistic philosophy is particularly regrettable since, as Goodwin points out in chapter 1, the biblical doctrine of creation provides a rational basis for assumptions essential to science. Western science began with men such as Copernicus, Galileo, Bacon, and Newton, who expected that they could understand the natural world because it was an artifact: a cosmos rather than chaos, and not simply the result of particles mindlessly interacting.

## Two Forms of Science

As it developed, Western science was conceived by its founders as making observations and devising logical explanations for how things worked, and testing these explanations via controlled experimentation (Bacon 1620). As Goodwin explains in chapter 1, there are two categories of science: "the *experimental* sciences...typically test hypotheses by doing multiple, controlled experiments under differing conditions. In contrast, the *historical* sciences...usually cannot directly test causal hypotheses by experiment." Distinguishing experimental (sometimes called empirical) from historical science is essential to understanding why Christians sometimes meet challenges when they engage in the scientific enterprise.

Rather than using repeatable experiments to establish their hypotheses, as is done in experimental science, practitioners of historical science rely on devising explanations, or "stories" (Lewontin 1997) that incorporate the data that have been collected, attempting to show how the data fit together and into the rest of what we know. In historical science, the test of any particular hypothesis is the scientific community's perception of the superior explanatory power of one story over another. No experimental confirmation is available, since historical science deals with past events. We must rely on inferences from the data collected, as well as our informed speculation about what might have occurred.

It is essential that we distinguish *historical* from *experimental* science when we talk about the tension between faith and science. As an exercise, ask yourself which of the two is referred to in the following examples from preceding chapters:

1. "[S]cience is a way to gain testable knowledge about nature" (chapter 1).
2. "[P]seudogenes have been found to be involved with essential functions" (chapter 2).
3. "One proposal is that life began not with proteins, but with RNA" (chapter 4).
4. "These methods use the regular, clock-like decay of radioactive isotopes in rock or bone to infer the age of geological samples" (chapter 5).

5. "If God created the earth to sustain life, we would expect to find that conditions on earth are designed for that purpose" (chapter 6).
6. "The biogeochemical homeostasis of our planet provides evidence of God's intention for the earth 'to be inhabited'" (chapter 7).

Other examples can be found, and your powers of critical thinking will increase as you use your awareness of the differences to distinguish between experimental and historical scientific claims.

In both experimental and historical science, new data may upset the current consensus, but the new consensus or paradigm is formed in different ways. In the experimental sciences, a new interpretation convinces us by the weight of multiple experimental programs that provide a convincing case that we have knowledge derived from the data. Doubters can go to the laboratory and redo the experiments personally to see the confirming results. As I write this, there is an uproar over reports that NASA experimenters have discovered a bacterial form that can use arsenic rather than phosphorus for its subsistence (Wolfe-Simon 2010). Many microbiologists are criticizing the results, with one critic scathingly describing the findings as "lots of flim-flam, but very little reliable information" (Overbye 2010). However, it seems unlikely that there will be any controversy by the time that you read these words. One way or the other, the issue will be settled.

It is true that longstanding controversies do sometimes arise in the experimental sciences. The role of *Heliobacter pylori* was controversial for more than a decade, as Barry Marshall bucked the medical establishment and the drug companies to establish that a bacterium, not stress and spicy foods, caused stomach ulcers (Academy of Achievement 2011). Even after he satisfied Koch's postulates on his own body, it took years before his demonstration was accepted. However, such debates are relatively rare in experimental disciplines.

In contrast, in historical science a proposed interpretation is convincing largely because good argumentation provides sufficient clarity about what the accumulated data mean. Yet what appears to be good argumentation or sufficient clarity to one person may look like a pretty weak case to someone else. For this reason, ongoing public and often heated controversies are more common in the historical sciences. Numerous examples can be found in this book, for instance, disputes over whether there is a single phylogenetic tree of life (chapter 2), the origin of language and grammar (chapter 3), the mystery of the Cambrian Explosion (chapter 5), and the question of where the universe's fine-tuning came from (chapter 6).

The point of bringing out these disputes is not to discredit historical science but to encourage critical thinking about *all* scientific pronouncements. The essential skill is to distinguish among the data themselves, and their interpretations. In the historical sciences, the stories that are told to make sense of the current empirical evidence sometimes will differ, with some practitioners convinced by one story while others favor a competing scenario. This is particularly striking when scientists with very different presuppositions examine the data and then produce an interpretation to explain them.

## Bias in Science

Why is the same story convincing to some and not to others? A general principle demonstrated by cognitive scientists (and discussed by Karl Bailey in chapter 3), provides a clue: what is already in one's mind is a powerful influence on one's perception of reality and what it means. Curiously, many persist in thinking that scientists somehow overcome such biases. Why else would advertising campaigns use physicians in their white lab coats when promoting a particular product (Lawrence 2009)? If the public did not see scientists as more objective than the general public, such advertising would not work—and would soon disappear.

Such preconceptions or biases may operate at different levels. At the individual level, the desire to please a superior can convince someone to stand for the consensus rather than join a revolution. Fear of losing research funding or the hope of gaining a position may powerfully influence an individual's thinking, especially when one is not conscious of these motives.

Bias also operates at a more corporate level in science. As noted in chapter 1, Thomas Kuhn recognized that science is normally done within a paradigm: an overarching view of a given field of study that guides the types of questions asked and the sorts of explanations offered (1962). Paradigms play a central role in scientific research—they focus the community's attention on problems that the paradigm judges to be important—but they also introduce bias, especially when they operate within arbitrary philosophical constraints. Some questions will never be asked. Some plausible explanations will be excluded outright.

The most fundamental source of bias, however, is the worldview of the person making the judgment, a point made by Leonard Brand (chapter 4). By *worldview* in this context, I mean whether one holds a materialistic (secular) or theistic perspective. Of particular relevance to the present discussion, philosophical materialism and a strong form of theism offer fundamentally different perspectives on the study of nature. I will illustrate the biasing power of a materialistic worldview in the next section, but here let me point out that worldview commitments help explain why both materialistic evolutionists and traditional biblical creationists continue to support their interpretations even in the face of contrary evidence (e.g., molecular evidence for design [chapter 2] and radiometric evidence for great age of life on earth [chapter 5], respectively). In both cases, these anomalies are set aside in the hope that some future discovery will either resolve the discrepancy or lead to a new paradigm that is consistent with their respective worldview commitments.

All scientists have biases, but the methods of science (including careful reasoning and peer review) help to hold these biases in check, especially in the *experimental* sciences. Even there, however, these methods are not foolproof. For example, a recent study showed that about a third of peer-reviewed medical research studies were exaggerated or wrong, according to subsequent research—results that applied even to the most highly cited studies (Ioannidis 2005). The author attributes this, not to fraud, but to "an intellectual conflict of interest that pressures researchers to find whatever it is that is most likely to get them funded" (Ioannidis quoted in Freedman 2010:80). Both researchers and their reviewers appear to be affected by what they already know or expect to find—even in fields where follow-up studies may confirm or refute published results.

This limitation likely will apply even more forcefully in the historical sciences, such as paleontology and historical geology, where experimental confirmation is not possible even in principle (see previous section), and where worldview may play a stronger role in the interpretation of data and the process of peer review. For example, dissenters from Darwinism sometimes have been unable to publish in the historical sciences when their results contradict materialistic assumptions (Bergman 2008). On the other hand, many Adventists have published actively in geology and paleontology (see case studies in chapter 5); fair-minded people capable of setting aside their prejudices exist almost everywhere. However, the potential for difficulties ought not be minimized or ignored.

Let me be clear as I end this section: I emphatically do *not* mean to imply that scientific research is worthless or should be ignored! However, remaining aware that scientists and their reviewers are human will help us avoid uncritical acceptance of even widely heralded research results—*especially* where experimental refutation is impossible.

## The Power of a Worldview

Let's explore the power of worldview with a case study. In preparation for this section, I encourage you to review Brand's analysis of Richard Dawkins's argument (chapter 4), which Dawkins developed in *Climbing Mount Improbable* (1996). Dawkins concedes that achieving information-rich novelties by chance is impossible, but he argues that "Darwinism is *not* a theory of random chance. It is a theory of random mutation plus *non-random* cumulative natural selection" (1996:75; emphasis in original).

Dawkins introduced cumulative natural selection in an earlier book, *The Blind Watchmaker,* and he illustrated the concept using the analogy of a monkey typing randomly on the computer (1986). He clearly showed that random typing would never arrive at the simple phrase, "Methinks it is like a weasel." However, a computer simulation, which Dawkins alleged to mimic cumulative natural selection, "found" the phrase in short order: after 41–63 generations of selective "breeding" in which the simulation cumulatively preserved any combination of letters that was closer to the target phrase than the previous one. It is curious that Dawkins used this analogy, which is teleological in form. Later in the same chapter he dismissed (correctly) its relevance to natural selection, because the computer knew what the target of selection was but evolution does not. "Evolution has no…target.… The 'watchmaker' that is cumulative natural selection is blind to the future and has no long-term goal" (1986:50). Despite this, Dawkins is still cited as an authority and comparably bad analogies continue to be used as support for what cumulative selection can achieve (e.g., Heim 2002).

Dawkins apparently reproduced the same mistake in *Climbing Mount Improbable.* He suggested that getting to the top is easy if we "locate the mildly sloping path" that leads there (1996:12). In real life, however, the path does not exist prospectively; the route to the top can be seen only in retrospect. Furthermore, there is no evidence that natural selection can produce information-rich complexity in a cumulative manner. I concur with Axe: "[T]he conclusion that complex adaptations *cannot* be very complex without running into feasibility problems appears to be robust" (2010:9; emphasis added).

In the face of these difficulties, why do Richard Dawkins and other Darwinists continue to champion cumulative natural selection? Richard Lewontin, Harvard geneticist and evolutionary biologist, describes well the power of a worldview commitment:

> We take the side of science in spite of the patent absurdity of some of its constructs, in spite of its failure to fulfill many of its extravagant promises of health and life, in spite of the tolerance of the scientific community for unsubstantiated just-so stories, because we have a prior commitment, a commitment to materialism. It is not that the methods and institutions of science somehow compel us to accept a material explanation of the phenomenal world, but, on the contrary, that we are forced by our a priori adherence to material causes to create an apparatus of investigation and a set of concepts that produce material explanations, no matter how counterintuitive, no matter how mystifying to the uninitiated.... The primary problem is not to provide the public with the knowledge of how far it is to the nearest star and what genes are made of.... Rather, the problem is to get them to reject irrational and supernatural explanations of the world, the demons that exist only in their imaginations, and to accept a social and intellectual apparatus, Science, as the only begetter of truth. (1997:31; emphasis in original)

This commitment to a materialistic worldview sometimes leads scientists to present as a finding of science what actually represents an article of faith in materialistic (or *naturalistic,* as used below) philosophy. For example, the late George Gaylord Simpson, eminent zoologist and vertebrate paleontologist, once claimed that despite incomplete knowledge, "it is already evident that all the objective phenomena of the history of life can be explained by purely naturalistic...factors." He boldly extended this conclusion to the origin of humanity: "Man is the result of a purposeless and natural process that did not have him in mind" (1949:343–344). Can you think of any way to test these statements empirically? I certainly cannot. In fact, Simpson appears to be simply expressing his worldview commitment, not describing the findings of scientific research.

Such statements convince many of us that philosophical materialism operates as a religion of sorts. This is not a new insight. Consider the opinion of Jakob von Uexkull, a German biologist who mentored the founders of ethology, Konrad Lorenz and Niko Tinbergen. "Darwinism, the logical consistency of which leaves as much to be desired as does the accuracy of the facts on which it is based, is *a religion rather than a science*. Consequently all arguments leveled against it rebound without effect; it is nothing but the embodiment of the impulse by the human will to get rid, by every possible means, of plan in Nature" (von Uexkull 1926:265; emphasis added).

As support for this claim, consider that Darwinists, working with a materialistic worldview, sometimes employ theological reasoning. For example, Leonard Brand notes that Darwinists often claim "that an intelligent God, an omniscient Designer, would never make organisms the way they are" (chapter 4). If Darwinism is empirical science, why do its adherents use what amounts to a theological argument in an attempt to defeat their rivals? Surely evidence-based argumentation should suffice. Recall that the rush to label much DNA "junk"—consistent with the Darwinist theological argument—was premature, with much of that "junk" now known to have function (chapter 2).

Let us sum up the argument: Many Darwinists show a firm commitment to a materialistic worldview in the face of contradictory evidence, a commitment that parallels the way many Christians remain unwilling to provide a criterion by which we will retain or abandon our belief in the life, death, and resurrection of Jesus Christ. Most Christians hold this belief as a matter of faith, however unlikely someone purports to show it to be. It seems that many Darwinists are doing the same with their core belief in materialism. There are, of course, exceptions. Anthony Flew, a famous and widely published lifelong atheist, has conceded that there must be a Mind outside of nature to explain the origin of the DNA code. He announced himself to be a Deist (Flew and Varghese 2008).

## How to Stop Fighting and Work Together

So, does all of this mean we are condemned to keep on fighting the (historical) science wars so long as time lasts? Given human nature, I suspect that we will, but it is certainly not necessary. What if we look at the belief continuum from atheism to theism, and think about how science and faith (both theistic and atheistic faith) might function as honest friends (chapter 1) rather than as adversaries. What might happen if, in pursuit of the best scientific understanding, some mavericks from each end of the faith spectrum begin to edge toward the mavericks on the other end—and they meet in the middle (Fig. 1)? Visualize a group in the center, looking similar to Leonard Brand's description of today's Intelligent Design (ID) Movement (chapter 4): scholars who conclude that current knowledge of the cell indicates at the very least, "Life on earth at its most fundamental level, in its most critical components, is the product of intelligent activity" (Behe 1996:193). Members of such a research group might have a variety of beliefs about common descent, the age of life on earth, and other historical scientific hypotheses. However, as they collaboratively investigate such questions, they commit to finding the best explanations based on empirical evidence.

If you've been reading about ID in the technical or popular scientific media, this probably sounds like a bad joke. Virtually all media are steeped in the materialistic worldview, however, so put what you have read (and watched) aside and think carefully. Traditional Christian theists are committed to the biblical story, and materialists are committed to nothing but matter and energy, so if both are determined to stand on the battlements shouting (and metaphorically shooting) at each other, a lot of collaborative historical science will not get done. Working together while holding these different perspectives might be good for historical science, as each side would help keep the other honest—detecting poor reasoning and refusing to accept shoddy work simply because it upholds existing beliefs. Peer

**Figure 1**—Model of the relationship involving creationism, Darwinism, and ID on the spectrum of theories about the history of life.

reviewers would be less likely to assume results to be valid simply because they agree with preconceptions (recall the study by Ioannidis 2005).

The Intelligent Design Movement currently includes various Christian theists, from six-day, young-earth creationists to long-age theistic evolutionists, as well as adherents of nontraditional faiths and even atheists. They get along because they do their best to keep each other honest, to avoid arguments over what is not part of empirical science, and to maintain an active awareness of their own presuppositions. Each holds personal opinions about historical science, but for the purpose of working together they have committed to tentatively accepting (or at least not fighting about) the best-supported, most logical interpretation of the currently available data. This approaches what is called the empiricist model for science: "the practice of relying upon observation and experiment esp. in the natural sciences" (Webster's 1963). The atheists swallow hard and avoid fights over the origins of the DNA code, the molecular machines in the cell (Meyer 2009), and other evidence that so strongly implicates a designer of some kind (of course, evidence cannot prove that God created—only His return will do that). In turn, we young-earth creationists acknowledge empirical challenges to our beliefs about the earth's age, and do not insist on making scientific conclusions beyond what the weight of current empirical evidence supports.

Certainly there are other issues, but these two are big ones. No one is asked to give up his or her beliefs, but all agree to subordinate their opinions to the current evidence and the most logical interpretation *while they are working together in the scientific realm.* It might be called, with a nod to C. S. Lewis, *mere science.* Materialists are free to do origin-of-life research and report their results. Creationists can attempt to show that methods of radiometric dating have flaws or that the data can rationally be interpreted as indicating youth. However, both sides know that they will be challenged to make their cases based on the current weight of evidence, and neither is allowed to derail the joint effort by evangelism or anathema.

As you might imagine, most materialists will have nothing to do with ID, which many view as simply a new form of creationism. Plenty of young-earth creationists likewise refuse to endorse or get involved with ID, because they believe that the subject of origins must be used for evangelism to win souls for Christ. Although I respect these fellow believers, I cannot agree that science is only worthwhile if it is directly applicable to evangelism.

Intelligent design is a way of doing science that aims to separate the scientific enterprise from the assumption of naturalism or any other faith commitment. This is an important goal in its own right. In the long run I expect that it will indirectly assist evangelism because truth will be discovered.

Many other fine Christian scientists also have nothing to do with ID, for various reasons. Some even lecture and write books against the movement, and any misrepresentations must be refuted whenever possible. Despite these critics, however, I urge each of you to begin (or continue) to read about ID and the evidence that supports this perspective. Doing historical science in this way is a bit like going back to the way Western science was practiced at its origin, only with a far larger knowledge base and the advantages technology brings.

## Why All This Matters So Much

At this point, someone in my class generally asks: "Dr. Aagaard, if we're scientists, and if the most logical interpretation of the current evidence indicates that the earth and its life are very old, why don't we just accept that, and dispense with the biblical story of a 6-day creation a short time ago?" This a fair question, and there are two parts to the answer. First, all human beings believe some things that are contradicted by what appears to be the most logical interpretation of the data. Remember Richard Dawkins and the origin of life? He is not particularly troubled that there are *no* credible data indicating that random events can produce the information essential to form life, nor later to generate the new information necessary for producing the incredible diversity that we see in the fossil record and alive on the earth today. So, a Christian who maintains his or her belief in recent Creation is doing no more than today's most outspoken atheist—retaining a belief essential to a worldview and awaiting additional evidence.

The second reason to hold on to Creation is the important one, however. The central story of Scripture, the story of Redemption, is what I have built my life around, and it is far more important to me than whatever the scientific community is saying at any given time. It appears to me that if we give up our belief in Genesis 1–11 as historically true, and then remain consistent about how we interpret Scripture, it is inevitable that in time we will stop being Christian in all but name. Think about this: Why are we urged to see Genesis as allegory or myth, not as historical reality? Although the interpretation of Genesis 1–11 has been a theological issue for centuries, much of the force of today's argument against a literal interpretation of those chapters is derived from the fact that some data of science (especially the fossil record and the results of radiometric dating) can logically be interpreted in ways that make the historicity of Genesis look problematic. If we follow the logic, however—questioning biblical historicity on the basis of current scientific interpretation—what do we say when asked about the biblical record of Jesus's birth, life, death, and resurrection? If we interpret the Gospels with the same hermeneutic we have just used on Genesis, what will be our decision about the historicity of what the Bible says about Jesus Christ? The empirical evidence against a virgin birth, the existence of a God-Man, the miracles described in the Gospels, and the Resurrection, is far stronger than that against a worldwide flood. There is exactly zero experimental evidence that a dead human being can be revivified. What then shall we believe about the story of Christ's sacrifice for us, and His continuing ministry in heaven, to say nothing of His second coming? Recall what Paul said about this in 1 Corinthians 15:17–19:

> And if Christ be not raised, your faith *is* vain; ye are yet in your sins. Then they also which are fallen asleep in Christ are perished. If in this life only we have hope in Christ, we are of all men most miserable. (KJV, emphasis added)

It is true that there are Christians who do not accept the first eleven chapters of Genesis as history but still affirm the orthodox Christian view of the Gospel accounts of Jesus's ministry, death, and resurrection. Without judging motives, we can observe that their position is not logically consistent because they apply different hermeneutical approaches to the two stories, an interpretive distinction not warranted by the text of Scripture itself. This position is unlikely to be stable in the long term. In fact, the trajectory described above—first abandoning Genesis as history and later giving up Christ's miracles, His bodily resurrection, and even His continuing existence—not only makes logical sense but also has been seen in the lives of individuals (Ham and Byers 2000), and even in churches. The mainstream Presbyterian Church in the United States abandoned a literal reading of Genesis a long time ago, but it was recently rocked when seminary professors began to teach that Christians do not need to accept either the bodily Resurrection or the Atonement (Williamson

2002). It is important that we decide whether we wish to follow others along this path, then let that decision guide our commitments.

## Conclusions

Let me now summarize the general points I find most important for a proper understanding of the issues under discussion.

1. Definitions really matter, and having a discussion without nailing down (and sticking to) the definitions of crucial concepts may be futile, if not counterproductive.
2. There are two kinds of science, often called *experimental* (or empirical) and *historical* sciences. Experimental (and not historical) science is what we usually think about when we hear the word *science,* but the distinction between the two kinds is not often made in our texts and other media. This appears to be unjustified, and may be motivated by metaphysical, rather than strictly scientific, considerations.
3. Everyone has a worldview, and everyone's worldview influences his or her interpretation of data. In historical science, worldview strongly influences, if it does not determine, whether one accepts the most logical current interpretation of the evidence or sets aside the problem. This is part of being human and is not characteristic solely of Christian believers.
4. Although creationism and Darwinism can be viewed as expressions of competing "religions," the ID paradigm (what some have called "mere science") offers a chance to do historical science without being driven by religious presuppositions (so far as is humanly possible).
5. The scriptural story of Creation is essential to the biblical worldview and therefore to the core of the Christian message, and if we give it up, we will in time lose the story of Redemption as a historical reality, and stop being Christians in the traditional sense altogether.

I urge you to study these issues with the attention that their importance warrants, certainly using this book as part of the project. Whatever you do, please do not drift into one position or another because of your fears, because of admiration for some respected figure, or for *any* reason other than your own informed judgment of what the scientific enterprise can (and cannot) tell us, as well as what truths are essential for a Christian getting ready for life in the New Earth. May God bless and guide you as you continue to mature in Him.

## Literature Cited

Academy of Achievement. 2011. Barry Marshall biography. Last revised Nov 7, 2005. Accessed online July 18, 2011, at: http://www.achievement.org/autodoc/page/mar1bio-1.

Axe, D. D. 2010. The limits of complex adaptation: An analysis based on a simple model of structured bacterial populations. BIO-Complexity 2010(4):1–10.

Bacon, F. 1620. Novum organum. Nabu Press, Berlin.

Behe, M. J. 1996. Darwin's black box. The Free Press, New York.

Bergman, J. 2008. Slaughter of the dissidents. Leafcutter Press, Southworth, Washington.

Campbell, N. A., J. B. Reece, and L. G. Mitchell. 1999. Biology, 5th ed. Benjamin Cummings, Menlo Park, California.

Dawkins, R. 1986. The blind watchmaker: Why the evidence of evolution reveals a universe without design. W. W. Norton, New York.

Dawkins, R. 1996. Climbing mount improbable. W.W. Norton, New York.

Flew, A., and R. A. Varghese. 2008. There is a God: How the world's most notorious atheist changed his mind. HarperOne, New York.

Freedman, D. H. 2010. Lies, damned lies, and medical science. Atlantic Magazine, November: 76–78, 80–82, 84–86.

Ham, K. and S. Byers. 2000. The slippery slide to unbelief. Creation Ex Nihilo 22(3):8–13.

Heim, W.G. 2002. Natural selection among playing cards. The American Biology Teacher 64:276–278.

Hirsch, E. D., J. F. Kett, and J. S. Trefil. 2002. The new dictionary of cultural literacy, 3rd edition. Houghton Mifflin, Boston.

Ioannidis, J. P.A. 2005. Contradicted and initially stronger effects in highly cited clinical research. JAMA 294:218–228.

Johnson, P. E. 1991. Darwin on trial. InterVarsity Press, Downers Grove, Illinois.

Johnson, P. E. 1998. Overestimating the power of science. Commonweal, June 5, 15–16.

Kuhn, T. S. 1962. The structure of scientific revolutions. University of Chicago Press, Chicago.

Lawrence, L. 2009. Cigarettes were once "physician" tested, approved. Clinical News in Oncology and Hematology. Published online March 10, 2009. Accessed online July 18, 2011, at: *http://www.hemonctoday.com/article.aspx*?rid=37712.

Lewis, C. S. 2001. Mere Christianity, 1st HarperCollins ed. HarperSan-Francisco, San Francisco.

Lewontin, R. 1997. Billions and billions of demons: Review of Sagan, C., The demon-haunted world: Science as a candle in the dark. New York Review of Books, January 9:28–32.

Meyer, S. C. 2009. Signature in the cell: DNA and the evidence for intelligent design. HarperOne, New York.

Overbye, D. 2010. Poisoned debate encircles a microbe study's result. The New York Times, published online December 13, 2010. Accessed online July 18, 2011, at: http://www.nyt.com/2010/12/14/science/14arsenic.html?43r=science.

Simpson, G. G. 1949. The meaning of evolution: A study of the history of life and of its significance for man. Yale University Press, New Haven, Connecticut.

Storer, T. I., and R. L. Usinger. 1965. General zoology, 4th edition. McGraw Hill, New York.

Uexkull, J. J. von. 1926. Theoretical biology. Kegan Paul, Trench, Trubner & Company, London. (Translated by D. L. Mackinnon.)

Webster's seventh new collegiate dictionary. 1963. G. & C. Merriam Company, Springfield, Massachusetts.

Williamson, P. T. 2002. The naked truth. The Layman, December 2002:5.

Wolfe-Simon, F. et al. 2010. A bacterium that can grow by using arsenic instead of phosphorus. Science, published online December 2, 2010. DOI: 10.1126/science.1197258.

# AFTERWORD

If you picked up this book in the first place, it is likely that you are a student of biology, but you may not be pursuing biology as a career (although I hope a few of our readers are!). Now that you have finished the book, you might still be wondering how the themes we have discussed apply to you—whether you are preparing for a career as a physician, dentist, pharmacist, psychologist, attorney, teacher, or perhaps professional biologist (among many possibilities). I cannot answer this question directly; only you can make the essential links between your learning and your life. However, I will offer a few suggestions, which I hope will be helpful.

First of all, do not forget that life is more than your career. It is our hope that on a personal level you have found satisfaction as you have come to a better understanding of the many ways Seventh-day Adventist faith shapes and interacts with biology. It is rewarding to note how Adventist biologists, motivated by a commitment to be true to the Scriptures while being honest in their study of science, have contributed significantly to better scientific understanding in a variety of areas (chapter 5). I also hope you now will be better able to share your faith with educated friends: to show by word and example that a thoughtful, scientifically informed individual can take seriously the biblical teaching of Creation while also fully engaging scientific evidence.

Also, I trust you are now better equipped to take up public roles in your communities and churches, where matters of faith and science will most certainly intersect. A number of topics treated in this book will surface in public discussions—for example, debates about creation and evolution (chapter 4), environmental stewardship (chapter 7), and how to apply genomic knowledge in ethical ways (chapter 2). It is our hope that you will be more informed now that you have read and reflected on these themes.

Second, a faith-informed understanding of biology will most likely be more relevant to your career than you think. Consider, for example, how a faith-based understanding of human nature and brain function (chapter 3) or environmental stewardship (chapter 7) might shape the practice of medicine. Might Adventist physicians have an edge in treating patients because of a biblically and scientifically informed belief that humans are integrated wholes, and because of a commitment to environmentally friendly ways of living: simplicity, Sabbath rest, and encouragement to vegetarianism to name a few? I would like to think so.

Third, the themes explored in this book will be relevant to you, even if you have little direct future contact with the study of biology. For example, a faith-based perspective on the fallibility of humans and human knowing applies to all other disciplines. This recognition should engender appropriate humility in us as we search for truth—whatever our career or field of study.

Finally, let us return to the metaphor introduced at the outset: faith and science as honest friends. Although the metaphor is imperfect, I hope that it has illuminated your understanding of three dimensions of the faith-science relationship: how faith informs and guides scientific thinking; how science may inform and confirm faith understandings; and the reality that in our current fallible condition, the two will not always agree. The latter point is no surprise, as the apostle Paul commented, "Now we see through a glass, darkly; but then face to face" (1 Corinthians 13:12, KJV). May we each commit to love God with all our heart, soul, and mind (Matthew 22:37) as we prepare for the day *when we will see clearly!*

H. Thomas Goodwin

# RECOMMENDED READING

Behe, M. J. 1996. Darwin's black box: The biochemical challenge to evolution. The Free Press, New York.
Behe, M. J. 2007. The edge of evolution: The search for the limits of Darwinism. Free Press, New York.
Bouma-Prediger, S. 2001. For the beauty of the earth: A Christian vision for creation care. Baker Academic, Grand Rapids, Michigan.
Brand, L. R. 2009. Faith, reason, and earth history, 2nd ed. Andrews University Press, Berrien Springs, Michigan.
Brown, W. S., and B. D. Strawn. 2012. The physical nature of Christian life: Neuroscience, psychology, and the church. Cambridge University Press Cambridge, United Kingdom.
Deane-Drummond, C. 2008. Eco-Theology. Saint Mary's Press, Winona, Minnesota.
Dunbar, S., L. J. Gibson, and H. M. Rasi (eds.) 2013. Entrusted: Christians and environmental care. Adventus International University Publishers, Mexico.
Gottlieb, R. S. 2006. A greener faith: Religious environmentalism and our planet's future. Oxford University Press, Oxford, United Kingdom.
Jeeves, M. A. 2013. Minds: A conversation on faith, psychology, and neuroscience. InterVarsity Press, Downers Grove, Illinois.
Meyer, S. C. 2009. Signature in the cell: DNA and the evidence for intelligent design. HarperOne, New York.
Meyer, S. C. 2013. Darwin's doubt. HarperOne, New York.
Murphy, N. C. 2006. Bodies and souls, or spirited bodies? Cambridge University Press, Cambridge, United Kingdom.
Roth, A. A. 1998. Origins: Linking science and scripture. Review and Herald, Hagerstown, Maryland.
Sanford, J. C. 2008. Genetic entropy and the mystery of the genome. FMS Publications, Waterloo, New York.
Shapiro, J. A. 2011. Evolution: A view from the 21st century. FT Science Press, Upper Saddle Press, New Jersey.

## Appendix A

# THE INSTITUTE FOR CHRISTIAN TEACHING

The Institute for Christian Teaching (ICT) was established in 1987, through the generous donation of a Seventh-day Adventist businessman, to promote excellence in Adventist education. Under the direction of an Advisory Committee and the supervision of the Education Department of the General Conference of Seventh-day Adventists, the Institute offers seminars and develops resources to foster the integration of faith and learning in Christian schools, colleges, and universities.

Since 1988 and with additional funding from the General Conference of Seventh-day Adventists and other donors, the Institute has sponsored international faith and learning seminars for educators in the United States as well as in Argentina, Australia, Bolivia, Brazil, Colombia, Côte d'Ivoire, England, France, Germany, India, Jamaica, Kenya, Korea, Mexico, Nigeria, Peru, Philippines, Singapore, South Africa, and Thailand.

The Institute for Christian Teaching pursues the following objectives:

1. To promote excellence—professional and spiritual—in Seventh-day Adventist teaching at the secondary and post-secondary levels.
2. To foster the integration of faith and learning throughout the curriculum on the basis of a comprehensive Christian worldview.
3. To focus on the uniqueness, values, and implications of Seventh-day Adventist educational philosophy.
4. To stimulate research and publication in the area of Christ-centered, Bible-based, and service-oriented education.

At present, the Institute has published more than 600 monographs on secondary, college/university, and professional topics, developed by participants in the faith and learning seminars. These can be obtained individually or in bound volumes in the *Christ in the Classroom* series. Some of these essays can be downloaded from our website, http://ict.adventist.org.

For a free catalogue of the materials available and information on upcoming seminars, contact:

The Institute for Christian Teaching
General Conference Education Department
12501 Old Columbia Pike
Silver Spring, MD 20904-6600, U.S.A.
Telephone: (301) 680-5060
Fax: (301) 622-9627
Website: http://ict.adventist.org
E-mail: rodrigueze@gc.adventist.org

# Appendix B

# THE CENTER FOR COLLEGE FAITH

The Center for College Faith is an initiative of Andrews University which seeks to help faculty better understand and foster the faith development of college undergraduates. Membership in the Center is open to all Andrews University faculty and is voluntary. The Center was formally organized in 1998, but its origin lies in a faculty convocation in 1996 which recognized a need to more effectively highlight faith development as central to the entire undergraduate experience.

The stated mission of the Center is twofold. First, we seek to acquire and disseminate knowledge about how college students develop in their Christian beliefs, values, and lifelong commitment to God, especially in relation to direct academic experiences. Second, we endeavor to promote on the Andrews University campus the growth of a distinctly Christian undergraduate "culture of learning" informed by careful scholarship.

Funded by generous donors, the Center has co-sponsored (with the Institute for Christian Teaching) the Faith and Learning Conference at Andrews University in 1999 and the publication of the Faith and Learning Series, of which the present volume is the fourth. Center activities include an active research initiative focused on the college impact on spiritual formation of undergraduates; a development program for Center faculty which supports professional growth, scholarship, and curricular revision pertinent to the Center's mission; a faculty seminar series to promote dialogue on issues of faith development; and the support for publishing scholarship at the interface of Christian faith and the Academy.

For further information, please contact the director of the Center:

Mickey D. Kutzner
Physics Department
Andrews University
Berrien Springs, MI 49104
(269) 471-6291
kutzner@andrews.edu

# Appendix C

# OFFICIAL SEVENTH-DAY ADVENTIST STATEMENTS

## Caring for Creation: A Statement on the Environment (1992)

The world in which we live is a gift of love from the Creator God, from "Him who made the heavens, the earth, the sea, and the springs of water" (Revelation 14:7; 11:17, 18). Within this creation He placed humans, set intentionally in relationship with Himself, other persons, and the surrounding world. Therefore, as Seventh-day Adventists, we hold its preservation and nurture to be intimately related to our service to Him.

God set aside the seventh-day Sabbath as a memorial and perpetual reminder of His creative act and establishment of the world. In resting on that day, Seventh-day Adventists reinforce the special sense of relationship with the Creator and His creation. Sabbath observance underscores the importance of our integration with the total environment.

The human decision to disobey God broke the original order of creation, resulting in a disharmony alien to His purposes. Thus our air and waters are polluted, forests and wildlife plundered, and natural resources exploited. Because we recognize humans as part of God's creation, our concern for the environment extends to personal health and lifestyle. We advocate a wholesome manner of living and reject the use of substances such as tobacco, alcohol, and other drugs that harm the body and consume earth's resources; and we promote a simple vegetarian diet.

Seventh-day Adventists are committed to respectful, cooperative relationships among all persons, recognizing our common origin and realizing our human dignity as a gift from the Creator. Since human poverty and environmental degradation are interrelated, we pledge ourselves to improve the quality of life for all people. Our goal is a sustainable development of resources while meeting human needs.

Genuine progress toward caring for our natural environment rests upon both personal and cooperative effort. We accept the challenge to work toward restoring God's overall design. Moved by faith in God, we commit ourselves to promote the healing that rises at both personal and environmental levels from integrated lives dedicated to serve God and humanity.

In this commitment we confirm our stewardship of God's creation and believe that total restoration will be complete only when God makes all things new.

*This statement was approved and voted by the General Conference of Seventh-day Adventists Executive Committee at the Annual Council session in Silver Spring, Maryland, October 12, 1992.*

## A Statement on the Environment (1995)

Seventh-day Adventists believe that humankind was created in the image of God, thus representing God as His stewards, to rule the natural environment in a faithful and fruitful way.

Unfortunately, corruption and exploitation have been brought into the management of the human domain of responsibility. Increasingly men and women have been involved in a megalomaniacal destruction of the earth's resources, resulting in widespread suffering, environmental disarray, and the threat of climate change. While scientific research needs to continue, it is clear from the accumulated evidence that the increasing emission of destructive gasses, the depletion of the protective mantel [*sic*] of ozone, the massive destruction of the American forests, and the so-called greenhouse effect, are all threatening the earth's eco-system.

These problems are largely due to human selfishness and the egocentric pursuit of getting more and more through ever-increasing production, unlimited consumption and depletion of nonrenewable resources. The ecological crisis is rooted in humankind's greed and refusal to practice good and faithful stewardship within the divine boundaries of creation.

Seventh-day Adventists advocate a simple, wholesome lifestyle, where people do not step on the treadmill of unbridled consumerism, goods-getting, and production of waste. We call for respect of creation, restraint in the use of the world's resources, reevaluation of one's needs, and reaffirmation of the dignity of created life.

*This statement was approved and voted by the General Conference of Seventh-day Adventists Administrative Committee (ADCOM) and was released by the Office of the President, Robert S. Folkenberg, at the General Conference session in Utrecht, the Netherlands, June 29–July 8, 1995.*

## A Statement on Stewardship of the Environment (1996)

It is the belief of the Seventh-day Adventist Church that humankind was created in the image of God, and is thus to represent God as His steward and to manage the natural environment in a faithful and fruitful way. Nature is a gift from God.

Unfortunately, men and women have been increasingly involved in an irresponsible destruction of the earth's resources, resulting in widespread suffering, environmental degradation, and the threat of climate change. While scientific research needs to continue, it is clear from the accumulated evidence that the increasing emission of destructive gasses, the massive destruction of the American rain forests, and the depletion of the protective mantel [*sic*] of ozone (the so-called greenhouse effect), are all threatening the earth's eco-system. There are dire predictions of global warming, rising sea levels, increasing frequency of storms and destructive floods, and devastating desertification and droughts.

These problems are largely due to human selfishness and greed which result in ever-increasing production, unlimited consumption, and depletion of nonrenewable resources. Solidarity with future generations is discussed, but the pressure of immediate interests is given priority. The ecological crisis is rooted in humankind's greed and refusal to practice good and faithful stewardship.

The government and people of Costa Rica are to be commended for their support of a comprehensive policy of sustainable development in harmony with nature.

Seventh-day Adventism advocates a simple, wholesome lifestyle, where people do not step on the treadmill of unbridled over-consumption, accumulation of goods, and production of waste. A reformation of lifestyle is called for, based on respect for nature, restraint in the use of the world's resources, reevaluation of one's needs, and reaffirmation of the dignity of created life.

*This statement was approved and voted by the General Conference of Seventh-day Adventists Administrative Committee (ADCOM) for release by the Office of the President, Robert S. Folkenberg, at the Annual Council session in San Jose, Costa Rica, October 1–10, 1996.*

## Appendix D

# FACULTY WITH ACTIVE ENVIRONMENTAL RESEARCH PROGRAMS[1]

### Andrews University (Michigan, USA)

- Daniel Gonzalez—animal behavior and ecology (mammals)
- H. Thomas Goodwin—ancient ecology (fossil vertebrates)
- James L. Hayward—animal behavior and ecology, ancient environments (birds, fossil vertebrates)
- Shandelle M. Henson—animal behavior and ecology (terrestrial invertebrates, birds)
- Kanya C. Long—ecology of infectious diseases (viruses, arthropods)
- Robert Zdor—plant physiological ecology (terrestrial plants)

### Canadian University College (Alberta, Canada)

- Noble T. Donkor—plant and animal ecology (terrestrial plants, mammals)

### La Sierra University (California, USA)

- Raul E. Diaz—animal ecology, systematics, developmental biology (amphibians, reptiles)
- L. Lee Grismer—animal ecology, systematics (amphibians, reptiles)
- John Perumal—plant ecology (terrestrial plants)
- Lloyd A. Trueblood—animal physiological ecology (marine invertebrates)

### Loma Linda University (California, USA)

- Leonard R. Brand—ancient environments (fossil vertebrates)
- H. Paul Buchheim—ancient environments (fossil invertebrates and vertebrates)

---

1. Faculty at North American Seventh-day Adventist colleges and universities with active research programs in environmental disciplines (as of January 2014).

- Ronald L. Carter—animal behavior and ecology, conservation, systematics (reptiles)
- Stephen G. Dunbar—marine biology, ecological physiology (marine invertebrates and vertebrates)
- David T. Dyjack—environmental health (humans)
- Ricardo Escobar—animal behavior and ecology, conservation, systematics (reptiles)
- Raul Esperante—ancient environments (fossil vertebrates)
- William K. Hayes—animal behavior and ecology, conservation, systematics (invertebrates, reptiles, birds)
- V. Leroy Leggitt—ancient environments (fossil invertebrates and vertebrates)
- Harold J. Marlow—environmental health (humans)
- Susanne B. Montgomery—environmental health (humans)
- Ronald Nalin—ancient environments (fossil invertebrates and vertebrates)
- Kevin E. Nick—ancient environments, environmental health (fossil invertebrates and vertebrates, humans)
- Joan Sabate—environmental health (humans)
- Ryan G. Sinclair—environmental health (humans)
- Samuel Soret—environmental health (humans)
- Padma P. Uppala—environmental health (humans)
- Seth Wiafe—environmental health (humans)

## Oakwood University

- Alexander G. Volkov—plant physiology (plants)

## Pacific Union College (California, USA)

- Floyd E. Hayes—animal behavior and ecology, conservation, systematics (marine invertebrates, birds)
- Shelton S. Herbert—animal behavior (reptiles)
- Aimee Wyrick—conservation (amphibians)

## Southern Adventist University (Tennessee, USA)

- Aaron G. Corbit—animal behavior and ecology (reptiles)
- Valerie A. Lee—animal behavior and ecology (birds)
- Benjamin J. Thornton—environmental toxicology (terrestrial

invertebrates)
- Neville A. Trimm—animal behavior and ecology (birds)

## Southwestern Adventist University (Texas, USA)

- Arthur V. Chadwick—ancient environments (fossil invertebrates and vertebrates)
- Amy M. McHenry—environmental health (protozoan parasites)
- Arthur G. Schwarz—plant ecology (terrestrial plants)

## Union College (Nebraska, USA)

- Corraine A. McNeill—animal behavior and ecology, agricultural entomology (invertebrates)
- Amy C. Utt—animal behavior and ecology, conservation (birds)

## Walla Walla University (Washington, USA)

- David L. Cowles—marine biology and ecological physiology (marine invertebrates)
- Robert A. Cushman, Jr.—ancient environments (plants and pollen)
- Joseph G. Galusha—animal behavior and sociobiology (birds)
- James R. Nestler—animal ecology and ecological physiology (marine invertebrates, birds, mammals)
- Kirt L. Onthank—animal ecology and ecological physiology (marine invertebrates)

# ABOUT THE AUTHORS

**Earl M. J. Aagaard** is enjoying retirement in Chico, California, after over 30 years of teaching biology. After teaching for several years at the academy level, Aagaard taught at Pacific Union College (1982–2004) and Southern Adventist University (2004–2009). He has a BS and an MA in biology from Pacific Union College, and a PhD from Colorado State University. Aagaard has strong interest in the relationship between science and faith, and he has authored several contributions in this field.

**Karl G. D. Bailey** is Associate Professor of Psychology and Director of the Behavioral Neuroscience Program at Andrews University. He has a BS from Andrews University (majors in biology and psychology) and both an MA and a PhD from Michigan State University. Bailey's scholarly interests and multiple technical contributions are in the fields of cognitive psychology and the psychology of motivation and religion. He joined the Andrews University faculty in 2004.

**Leonard Brand** is Professor of Biology and Paleontology at Loma Linda University, where he has taught since 1969. He earned a BA in biology from La Sierra College, an MA from Loma Linda University, and a PhD from Cornell University. Brand is author of several books that explore the interface of science and Christian faith, including *Faith, Reason, and Earth History* (Andrews University Press, 2009), *Beginnings* (with David Jarnes; Pacific Press, 2006), and *Choose You This Day* (coauthor Richard Davidson; Pacific Press, 2013). He also has authored multiple scientific papers in the fields of animal behavior and paleontology.

**David L. Cowles** is Professor of Biology at Walla Walla University. Cowles earned a BS and an MS in biology from Walla Walla College, and a PhD from University of California, Santa Barbara. His fields of interest include marine biology and ecological physiology, and he has published multiple papers in these fields. Cowles taught at Loma Linda University (1987–2001) before joining the Walla Walla faculty in 2001.

**H. Thomas Goodwin** is Professor of Paleobiology and Chair, Department of Biology, at Andrews University. He earned a BA from Southern Adventist University (majors in biology and theology), an MA from Loma Linda University, and a PhD from the University of Kansas. He has published multiple papers in the fields of mammalogy and paleobiology. Goodwin taught at Loma Linda University (1990–1994) before joining the Andrews faculty in 1994.

**Floyd E. Hayes** is Professor of Biology at Pacific Union College. He earned a BS from Loma Linda University, an MS from the University of Michigan, and a PhD from Loma Linda University. Hayes's research interests center on the ecology, behavior, and biogeography of birds, and he has published numerous scientific papers in these fields. Before joining the faculty at Pacific Union College in 2003, Hayes taught at Caribbean Union College (1993–1997) and the University of the West Indies (1997–2002).

**William K. Hayes** is Professor of Biology and Director of the Center for Biodiversity and Conservation Studies, Loma Linda University. He earned a BS and an MS in biology from Walla Walla College and a PhD from the University of Wyoming. He has published extensively on the behavioral ecology and conservation of birds and reptiles, with special interest in the ecological roles of snake and invertebrate venoms. Hayes taught at Southern Adventist University (1990–1995) before joining the Loma Linda faculty in 1996.

**Timothy G. Standish** is a Research Scientist at the Geoscience Research Institute, where he has served since 2001. He also teaches Molecular Genetics at Loma Linda University and classes in science and faith for the Adventist International Institute for Advanced Studies and Adventist University of Africa. He earned a BS in zoology, an MS in biology from Andrews University, and a PhD from George Mason University. Standish has authored numerous publications on the relationship between science and faith as well as several technical papers in molecular genetics. Before joining the Geoscience Research Institute, he taught at Union College (1992–1997) and Andrews University (1997–2001).

# INDEX

# D



# E

## T



## U



## V



## W



## Y



## Z